SEX IS NOT COMPULSORY

SEX IS NOT COMPULSORY

Giving up sex for better health and greater happiness

Liz Hodgkinson

COLUMBUS BOOKS
LONDON

First published in Great Britain in 1986 by
Columbus Books Limited
19-23 Ludgate Hill, London EC4M 7PD

British Library Cataloguing in Publication Data
Hodgkinson, Liz
    Sex is not compulsory: giving up sex for
    better health and greater happiness.
    1. Celibacy
    I. Title
    306.7'32   HQ800.15
ISBN 0–86287–229–4

Phototypeset by Falcon Graphic Art Ltd,
Wallington, Surrey
Printed and bound by
The Guernsey Press, Guernsey, Channel Islands

Contents

Introduction

During the 1960s, when the so-called sexual revolution was at its height, I believed that the world could be made a better and happier place if only we were able to shed our inhibitions, repressions and hang-ups about sex.

In those days I was truly convinced, like many other young people of my generation, that if we could reverse the narrow-minded, intolerant, fearful and sternly moralistic attitudes of previous generations we could all become more loving, more warm-hearted, more creative, vital and attractive.

Most of the sex advice books written during this period underlined the idea that the world could be saved by sex – provided of course that adequate contraceptive measures were taken at the same time. The ultimate quest of our generation was to experience more and more transcendent sex – without, of course, enduring the messy and inconvenient complications of an unwanted pregnancy. Many therapists of that era encouraged their neurotic and mentally disturbed patients to 'find themselves' and become better balanced individuals through positive experiences of sex. Sometimes surrogate partners would be provided for the purpose. We liked to believe then that much mental illness, and possibly a certain amount of physical illness as well, resulted from long-held repressions, and that these could be released through sex.

Those were the days of naked 'encounter' groups, of the rapid growth of the *Playboy* empire, and of the introduction of the 'Page Three girl'. At the same time, ever more explicit pornography and 'how-to' books about sex were published. Suddenly, it seemed that we needed to be told in precise anatomical detail how to perform the sexual act – something people had somehow managed to do without diagrams for many centuries previously.

Now, twenty years later, I no longer believe that ever-more-frequent sex has the power to make the world a better place. Though I would not advocate a return to the dark days of the nervous, frightened attitudes to sex which characterized some previous generations, I am certain that human problems and difficulties can never be resolved through physical sex. Nor do I believe that sex brings people together in any real or lasting way, or that it can clear the mind and enhance creativity. I now know that sex does not and cannot contribute to either mental or physical health.

In fact, my views about sex are in many ways the complete opposite of those I held a couple of decades ago. The reason for this is that with increasing maturity I have been able to observe for myself that more frequent physical sex has not added one jot to the sum of the world's happiness. Rather, it has probably been instrumental in compounding the sum of human misery.

We now have more divorces than at any other time in history, more young people are attempting suicide, and the number of those addicted to drugs and other mind-altering substances is going up all the time. In addition, the state of people's health, in every country, is extremely precarious. The incidence of heart disease and cancer is increasing, while more and more people are suffering from stress-related conditions.

Though we cannot blame all the world's present problems on the amount of sexual activity taking place, it is the case that much modern malaise can be directly or indirectly related back to sexual attitudes.

We have come to believe that we 'need' sex, that we have a God-given right to sexual satisfaction, and this has led us to exploit other people's bodies to release our own frustrations. Cases of rape and the sexual abuse of children have become terrifyingly commonplace and are starting to worry men as well as women. Furthermore, the search for sex is making us ever more restless, anxious and afraid.

As I once believed that sex was the answer to many deep-seated human difficulties, so I am now certain that a positive commitment to celibacy is the sensible way forward. Now celibacy – once exalted as a higher ideal than a sexually active existence – has in recent decades become very unpopular. So unpopular is it that there are currently moves to allow Catholic priests, almost the only celibate-by-choice people left in Western society, to marry and still remain members of the clergy.

Celibacy has come to be regarded with extreme distaste, because we have been led to believe that sex is (a) necessary and (b) natural. In fact, it is neither. Apart from its purpose in propagating the species, sex is no more necessary to our daily lives than a glass of whisky or a cream bun. All the celibate people I interviewed during the course of this book have spoken of the benefits of the non-sexual life, and have claimed that it is celibacy, rather than sex, which frees the individual and confers happiness. Celibacy, according to its adherents, can make people stronger in themselves, more autonomous, more self-confident and certainly more creative and intelligent. It also brings about an improved state of physical health.

It seems to me that celibacy, rather than sex, can enhance health and general well-being. One of the most important ways it can do this is that it reduces the amount of stress and sex hormones circulating in the system. Wildly fluctuating hormone levels, which always accompany sexual activity, have the effect of decreasing resistance to many illnesses, and reducing the body's ability to withstand infections.

A few years ago, the very idea of celibacy for non-religious people would hardly have been entertained. Probably few people would have been interested even in reading a book on the subject. Indeed, publisher Anthony Blond, in his *The Book Book*, stated that celibacy as a subject practically guaranteed nil sales.

Now, however, things have changed dramatically. We have all become aware that the sexual revolution has not delivered what it promised and that we are more confused, more bewildered, more unhappy than we were before. But also, diseases related to sex have become a frightening world-wide epidemic. AIDS in particular, a fatal disease for which no cure has yet been developed, has forced people to reappraise their sexual attitudes and ask whether there are better, healthier and more satisfying ways of relating to other people than by having sex with them.

Celibate people, it need hardly be said, do not succumb to AIDS. Neither do they catch herpes simplex, another incurable sexually transmitted disease (STD), and celibate women never have cervical cancer. In addition, the stress and blood-pressure rates of celibates are lower, and the incidence of heart disease and cancer among them is far lower. Celibate people, on the whole, live lives that are healthier than those of people who have promiscuous sex. They smoke and drink less, are more likely to be vegetarian and are considerably less likely to succumb to any kind of addiction.

But the biggest plus for celibates is that they usually find their relationships with other people are improved. As they are non-sexual they tend to see others as individual human beings, rather than simply as bodies which can be categorized attractive or not attractive and accepted or rejected as such. At the same time, they do not suffer to such a great extent from the negative emotions associated with an active sex life, such as greed, jealousy, lust, possessiveness, dependence and anger.

Celibacy emancipates both men and women from their dependency and over-reliance on each other, and enables them to be friends rather than enemies. George Bernard Shaw observed nearly a hundred years ago that the greatest stumbling block to female emancipation was lust, both female and male. We still have not heeded his advice, and many feminists continue to believe that more and better sex is the way to liberation.

Many people are frightened even to think about celibacy because they imagine that such a way of life is impossible. However, most people who are celibate because it is one of the requirements of their religious vocation say that chastity is actually the easiest of their disciplines and the 'secular celibates' also say they have not found giving up sex any kind of problem. We have, unfortunately, come to see wild, frequent sex as the norm whereas, in fact, a positive commitment to celibacy frees both body and spirit.

You may ask: if the whole world suddenly became celibate, what would happen to future generations? My answer to that is that the world never will become celibate, so it is a hypothetical question of little significance. But if the world were to be celibate for only a year, the global population problem would be solved. At the same time, the incidence of AIDS, herpes, cervical cancer and other STDs would instantly decrease.

When I speak about positive celibacy, I do not mean that sexual desires should be rigorously repressed and sublimated or that it is necessary to resort to a regime of cold baths and puritanical habits. If one thinks about sex all the time and has to deny oneself, celibacy has no value. It is only when there is no desire for sex that there is benefit.

A desire for sex lessens when there is understanding of what the sex drive, sexual frustration and sexual fulfilment are all about. This I shall try to explain in the chapters that follow. We have been afraid to 'let go' of sex because we do not really understand what it is. Once we do, its hold on our lives can be reduced.

I am not saying that henceforth everybody in the entire world should be celibate forever. That is both impossible and unrealistic. What I am saying is that most of us have never even considered celibacy as a way of relating to other people. Now is the time to realize that we have another option – a non-sexual one.

The prevailing myth has been that the only proper way to live is by having an active and varied sex life. We have not understood that its alternative, celibacy, can actually have much to recommend it. But it can never be positive while it is seen as giving something up. It is only when definite benefits of celibacy are seen that sex can be relinquished. I am sure that celibacy, not necessarily as a commitment for ever and ever, but as an option at certain crucial times in a person's life, has far more advantages than a desperate searching for bigger and better orgasms.

As we do not have to be sexual, neither do we have to be celibate if we do not want to be. All I am saying is: why not consider it? Since sex has patently not worked any magic, or brought about any long-term contentment, it is perhaps time to think about other, possibly more rewarding, ways of living one's life.

CHAPTER 1

Does sexual desire really exist?

Most people have come to assume that human beings possess something called 'sexuality' and that we all have an innate sexual urge. Indeed, those who do not appear to possess this characteristic are often seen as lacking, or 'dysfunctioning', in some way. As a result, celibacy is usually seen as unnatural, peculiar and perhaps even downright dangerous.

Many writers have drawn attention to the fact that a considerable proportion of the world's wickedest men – Hitler is always proffered as a prime example – were relatively uninterested in sex, and that was one reason they were able to perpetrate such atrocities. The Spanish Inquisition, it is often pointed out, was composed mainly of clerical celibates. It has been taken for granted in our century that sexual energies, if not channelled into their 'proper' outlet, will soon find other, more pernicious, means of expression.

In his *History of Western Philosophy* Bertrand Russell states: 'Liberation from the tyranny of the body contributes to greatness, but just as much to greatness of sin as to virtue.'

Many of the world's most famous sexologists, from Marie Stopes and Havelock Ellis to Kinsey and Masters and Johnson, have felt that prolonged lack of a sexual outlet could actually lead to severe mental and physical problems. If sexuality was denied its natural expression, they argued, it would be contained in the body where it would eventually manifest as stress and frustration, or worse.

Physical sex is commonly seen as a way of releasing pent-up feelings which it would be harmful to keep within the body. The 'frustrated spinster' of the past has traditionally been considered a figure of fun. Her frustration, of course, was seen to stem from the fact that she was

13

not having any sexual intercourse, and this in itself made her dried-up, intolerant, narrow-minded and puritanical. Also, it meant that she was unlikely to understand human nature, or be warm-hearted and tolerant.

In the old days, it was thought that sex used up energies which would then be unavailable for other, perhaps more elevated, pursuits. The Victorians thought that a man should not 'spend' too much semen, and Gandhi also adhered to this idea, which goes back to ancient Hindu scriptures. In the twentieth century, we have turned this idea completely on its head and have taken the view that sexual intercourse actually contributes to, rather than takes away from, bodily and mental energy. The sexologists of our times have taught us to believe that sex is natural, healthy, a basic need, and entirely necessary for human happiness and well-being.

The net result of extensive work by sexologists has led us to understand that there is such a thing as sexual desire, that the urge to intertwine physically with another person is as fundamental a drive as the need to eat, drink, sleep and find shelter. We ignore the sexual side of our natures at our peril, they have warned us, and we have taken their pronouncements as gospel.

To arrive at their conclusions, Alfred Kinsey and later researchers, notably Shere Hite, interviewed literally thousands of fellow Americans and undertook surveys that sometimes went on for years. They also evolved painstaking laboratory methods of measuring human sexual response to a variety of stimuli. Masters and Johnson, particularly, found laboratory methods helpful to their research.

I, unlike the sexologists, have not interviewed thousands of people, nor have I undertaken complicated computer analyses to find out exactly how many millimetres the clitoris expands under stimulation, or precisely which electrical and chemical pathways are involved in penile erection. Nor do I believe this sort of research is necessary when trying to come to conclusions about sexual desire. A few commonsense observations will tell us that, while sex is undoubtedly a very powerful drive, we as humans can, if we choose, live perfectly well without it. We need to have sexual intercourse in order to propagate the species, of course – although with *in vitro* methods of fertilization even this is becoming increasingly unnecessary – but we do not need to have sex in order to survive ourselves.

My own belief is that there is no such thing as purely *sexual* desire or *sexual* frustration. What we call arousal, frustration and satisfaction are actually generalized mental feelings that we have in recent times, for some reason, ascribed to the genital area. I shall try to explain why I think this is in the course of this chapter.

If we look at the animal kingdom – and biochemically we are extremely close to certain animals – we will find that none of them has any desire for sex except when there is a possibility of reproduction. Cat- and dog-owners know that their pets mate only at certain times – the female when she is on heat and the male when he perceives that there is a receptive female in the vicinity. Unless she is on heat, the female will show no sexual interest whatever in the male and will simply ignore his advances.

Those who are suspicious that we can draw worthwhile analogies with the animal kingdom cannot help but be aware that many millions of humans can and do live completely satisfactory and fulfilled lives without ever having physical sex. Monks and nuns in religious communities are, in the main, perfectly happy and healthy and in fact tend to live longer and succumb to far fewer degenerative diseases, such as cancer and heart conditions, than their peers in the outside world.

There is no evidence whatever that these avowed celibates live in a perpetual agony of sexual frustration, or that they have to 'relieve' themselves periodically by vigorous masturbation. Nor is there any evidence to suggest that homosexuality is more rampant in monastic life than in the outside world. In fact, it appears that celibacy is actually the very easiest of the many disciplines religious people choose to follow.

Those who are deprived of sex because they are, for example, in prison, widowed or on an Antarctic expedition do not usually speak of the miseries of sexual frustration during the period when a sexual relationship was denied to them. Many, many spinsters have lived happy, useful and productive lives without ever thinking about fulfilling themselves sexually – Florence Nightingale and Jane Austen are names which spring immediately to mind. They did not go into a decline owing to lack of sexual outlets – Florence Nightingale lived to be over 90. If sex was as basic a need as some sexologists aver, she would have been dead of frustration long before this age.

The fact that so many creative people have been able to live without sex – Botticelli, George Bernard Shaw, Cliff Richard, Andy Warhol, Emily Brontë, Virginia Woolf, Gandhi, Jesus Christ, St Paul – should lead us to question whether physical sex really is part of a necessary package if one wishes to lead a full, varied and useful life.

In Victorian days and earlier it was assumed that women, in the main, did not have any sexual feelings at all. Now, survey after survey in magazines and newspapers seems to indicate the opposite. A recent one which appeared in the *Daily Express* stated: 'The Modern Miss . . . likes sex as much as men do, and isn't afraid to say so.' This is what we like to believe, yet there are still many thousands of women who never experience any erotic sensations whatever – whether or not they are having regular sex.

In her book *The Limits of Sex* Celia Haddon writes: 'Sex without any sexual sensation is common among us women. Most of us have experienced it several times.' Do these women who never experience sexual sensations have a sex drive or not? If not, what happens to their 'sexual desire'? Kinsey, who firmly believed that all humans need sex, found during his researches that two out of every 100 women had never experienced sexual feelings of any kind – ever. And these were women who were having intercourse, not perpetual virgins. A later researcher, Geoffrey Gorer, discovered in his studies on marriage that one in a hundred marriages was sexless, and that in the later stages of wedlock sex usually became increasingly unimportant to both partners. Does sexual desire, then, disappear during marriage? If so, what happens to it?

Gabrielle Brown, author of a book called *The New Celibacy* which created a furore when it was published in America in 1980, said that physical sex could actually be considered a waste of time and energy. We are now ashamed, she wrote, if we do not have sexual feelings, and we have come to view almost any kind of frustration as having a sexual basis. When Dr Brown wrote in her book that more and more Americans were abstaining from sex and enjoying it, there were howls of disbelief on both sides of the Atlantic. So immersed are we nowadays in the idea that sex is vital that we find it hard to countenance anything which suggests the opposite – namely, that sex is not important, or need not be.

Our present beliefs about sex have, of course, been engendered mainly by the father of psychoanalysis, Sigmund Freud, who propounded that sexual fantasies played a large part in the behaviour of every pre-adolescent child. Freud believed that human beings are innately sexual, and that most non-sexual activities are actually a 'sublimation' of sexual feelings. We can, if we so wish, channel our sexuality into other areas, but we must recognize the source of these energies.

Freud said that small children are attached to their parents in fundamentally sexual ways – though as this is all in the subconscious neither they nor their parents may be aware of it – and also said that children have a fantasy desire to marry the parent of the opposite sex. He claimed that the root cause of many neuroses lies here. If we are unable to resolve sexual conflicts in ourselves, we may succumb to mental illness. It is now thought that much of what Freud presented as psychological disorder – for example, young women harbouring fantasies of being raped by their fathers – actually happened, and that the rapes were real, not the fancies of a disordered mind. But we will come to that in greater detail later (pages 92-3).

When Freud first published his theories – and it has to be stated that they were only *theories*, not actual proven facts – people were shocked beyond belief by the concept of innocent children being tainted with sexual thoughts. Now, conversely, we are shocked at the idea that there may be people around who do *not* have sexual feelings. To be asexual nowadays is to be considered only half human. In fact, we do not believe there is such a thing as an asexual person. Those who have little interest in sex are merely sublimating their feelings, we believe.

Things have got to such a pitch that we have come to the conclusion that everybody – even the disabled and the mentally handicapped – has a 'right' to sexual expression and should not be denied this form of fulfilment. The elderly, too, should have regular sex, we are told. No matter if they are long past the age of reproduction. In his book *Sex and the Over-forties* Robert Chartham, who has made large sums of money from sex books, describes cases of couples in their sixties, seventies and even eighties who are somehow still managing to have sex.

Exploring the question of whether or not humans are innately sexual, Gabrielle Brown says that the more interesting a person's life is in other respects the less likely a man or woman is to feel the lack of sex. In other words, sex can provide entertainment and excitement in an otherwise fundamentally empty and purposeless life.

It is certainly true that the more bored a person is – as for example when on holiday – the more likely he or she is to think about sex. Workaholic men, the types who are at their desks at seven a.m. and who take their files on holiday, commonly find that they are actually unable to have sex, as their work takes up all their capacity, and they become impotent. Do these people have sexual desire, or is it sublimated? Or is it merely that the whole of their energies are occupied with other matters?

Abraham Maslow, one of the founders of the so-called 'human potential' movement in the 'fifties in America, believed that the higher the level one lives at the less important and central to life are the 'lower' needs and their frustrations. The more otherwise empty a person's life, the more important sex will become.

Sex may appear important when life is boring and empty, but is it a real need? Even Masters and Johnson, who researched every possible aspect of sexual response, said that sex was the only physical process which could be denied for a lifetime without necessarily having ill effects. If you do not drink for a week you will be dead; if you do not eat for a week you will be extremely hungry; and if you do not excrete waste matter your body will be in a state of acute discomfort. You cannot manage without sleep, either.

But health, intelligence, mental functions and alertness

are not adversely affected by lack of sex. In fact, the opposite seems to be true. Once a person chooses to do without sex, intelligence, mental functions and alertness actually improve. One can look up instead of down, elevate oneself instead of being debased. It is perhaps most helpful to compare sex with an addiction to a mind-altering substance such as alcohol or nicotine. The more the habit is indulged, the more tolerance builds up and the less one imagines it is possible to do without it. But if the source of the addiction is removed, in time the habit and the dependence will lessen. Sexual frustration does not increase and build up if sex does not take place. Conversely, one gradually starts to forget about it.

As children, none of us experienced the slightest desire to smoke or drink, and usually the first few experiences of either are decidedly unpleasant. But in time, for some at least, pleasure is found and a dependence is established. Then, eventually, it may become uncomfortable to do without them for any length of time. Though the body may actually come to crave these substances, it does not actually need or want them, and in time will function less effectively with them. But mind-altering substances can also alter the workings of bodily cells, which is why such discomfort is felt when the addict is denied a fix.

So it is with sex. The body does not actually need sex, but a habit can be established whereby it comes to be seen as a basic need. While we have never had sex, we never miss it, but as with any other addiction, once the habit has become ingrained acute discomfort can be experienced if we are deprived of it. The big problem with sex, of course, unlike other addictions, is that it requires the co-operation of another person – willing, coerced or bought. Sexual frustration can be partially relieved by masturbation, but most sex addicts would agree that it is a poor substitute for the real thing.

As small children, most of us regard sex with something approaching horror and disbelief. The average 6-year-old's response on learning the facts of reproduction are: 'But isn't it a dirty job?' Many children will actively deny that their parents partake in such an unlikely activity. It is simply impossible for them to imagine.

Later, of course, we come to experience sensations

which we may interpret as sexual. As teenagers, we fall in love and may long to become one with the object of our desire. Both boys and girls imagine that the ultimate in bliss must be to spend a night in intimate union with the one they love.

This is the 'urge to merge', as Gabrielle Brown puts it. If, however, this desire is not satisfied or given expression, in time it simply goes away. It does not build up and up into uncontainable agony in a physical way. It is quite unlike, for example, the desire to pass water. The reason for this is that the desire for sex is not primarily a physical need, but one which originates in the mind. It is an *imagined*, not a real need.

We have been given to understand that sexual intercourse can be a way to personal happiness and fulfilment but, as with alcohol and nicotine, once the habit has been established, there is no possible way of ever having enough. One may feel, after a night of unbridled passion, that desire has been satisfied, but after a few hours it will come back again, worse and more urgent than ever – as if it had never been satisfied in the first place. All sexual intercourse does is create a desire to have more. And there is never any way of satisfying the craving.

In our society sex and love have become synonymous. This has not been so in all societies. In ancient and medieval times chaste, or platonic, love was seen as the ideal. But now it is believed that if you love somebody you will of necessity have sexual desire for him or her. An asexual love is considered extremely odd nowadays. 'Intimacy' is usually taken to mean sexual intimacy, and sex is considered a natural expression of love for another person. But, as I shall try to show in the course of this book, sex has nothing whatever to do with love. In fact, the more you truly love a person, the less you will want to have sex with him or her, for through sex a person is basically seeking to satisfy selfish desires. The needs, wishes and thoughts of the other person are rarely taken into consideration.

Few people who are 'in love' in the modern interpretation of the expression truly have the best interests of the other person at heart. In fact, once sex enters into the relationship it brings all kinds of negative, rather than positive, emotions into being. Once there is sex, there is also automatically anger, greed, lust, jealousy, possessiveness, domination, dependence and attachment. Sex takes away rather than giving anything positive to a relationship, as it removes an individual's innate coping mechanisms and makes him/her dependent upon another person for happiness, or what that individual considers to be happiness.

Married men – or those in a long-term partnership – will know just how often they have to beg their partners for sex, or wheedle them into it. They may have to use moral and emotional blackmail, physical force, threats and punishments in order to force the other person into agreeing to sex. Even in our supposedly sexually liberated days, many women know they have to pretend to have a headache, be fast asleep or too tired, so that their husbands – people for whom they have long ceased to feel the slightest desire – will not bother them for sex.

What, then, happens to sexual desire in a marriage or other long-term relationship? Is the man – or the partner who most wants sex – thinking of the best interests of the other person when threats and insults are used in order to gain sex? Where is the happiness that results when two people are in conflict about their sex lives? I do not know of a single relationship based on sex where the sex has not at some time or other been a source of unhappiness, argument and contention.

I do not believe we as humans possess genuine sexual desire. What we do have is a desire for intimacy, to blend with another person, to have our pain eased by that other person. There is also, in some people, a desire for domination, a wish to use other people's bodies for one's own gratification. There is sexual addiction, which builds up and may become an ingrained habit until the need appears insatiable. There is also, in some, the urge to possess another person completely, both body and soul, and have him/her in one's power. Some women exert power over men by behaving in sexy and tantalizing ways; many men exert power and control over women by forcing them into sex, either by actually raping them, or by hurling insults at them, such as calling them 'frigid' or accusing them of having no 'libido'.

21

Sex can be bought and sold; prostitution, the world's oldest profession, still flourishes in every country in the world. Sex can be used as currency, and is bartered in any sexual relationship, at least on occasion. If the husband brings his wife breakfast in bed, for instance, it is often understood that she will 'reward' him later with sex. Only rarely, except perhaps in the very early stages of a relationship, is sex freely exchanged.

One American researcher, Elizabeth Haich, has put it succinctly: 'Sexuality mimics love. It compels tenderness and embraces, it forces the lovers to hug one another, to allay one another's pain through the revelations of sexuality, as when true love is exchanged. What follows such experiences? Disappointment, a bitter aftertaste, mutual accusations or bleak loneliness, feelings of exploitation and defilement. Neither of the two gave true love, but only expected to receive it, therefore, neither received it.'

True love is giving, whereas sex is essentially taking. You are trying, in sex, to take the 'essence' from the other person and receive it yourself. But, one has to ask: is it right that another person should expect to be able to use my body for his/her own gratification? Should I supply my body to a sexual addict? Would I give heroin to a heroin addict? Sex is essentially about exploitation, not love. If it were not, it would not be a multi-billion-pound industry. Sex goes with violence, as in sex-and-violence novels and films. It goes with pornography, with prostitution and with wrecked mental and physical health. There are, as we know, many sexually transmitted diseases, of which AIDS is the latest and most worrying. You cannot get any disease from love. Sex can kill – love cannot.

If you truly love a person, you will naturally want what is best for that person. With sex, you want what you consider is best for yourself – bigger and better orgasms, more ecstatic experiences. Even if you attempt to 'satisfy' your partner – a patent impossibility – you are really doing it again only for self-gratification, so that you can earn a reputation as a good lover. There is little real attention paid to making the other person happy, and with sex a trade-off is always expected. Subconsciously, we know that to engage in intimate bodily contact means that a form of currency is being exchanged. Once a woman gives herself to a man, she expects something in return – whether this is lasting love and commitment, a fur coat, a dinner, marriage – the price changes according to the woman and the expectations of society, but a price is always extracted.

I believe that sexual desire is not innate but that we have, for convenience, for complicated emotional reasons, decided to concentrate desires, expectations and frustrations on the genital area.

So, one may ask at this point, what about the erogenous zones? Am I honestly suggesting, by proclaiming that there is no such thing as purely sexual desire, that erogenous zones do not exist? For we all know that in contemplation of sex with a loved one, nipples become erect, a tingling sensation is felt all over and there is a spontaneous reaction in the genital area – penile erection for men and vaginal discharge for women. If these sensations were not relieved through sex, one might have to take refuge in masturbation.

But again, there is a strong physiological case for saying that the erogenous zones are not really erogenous zones. They are merely areas of extra sensitivity which are supplied with more nerve endings than other parts of the body. The areas we call erogenous are extra-sensitive because they need protection, and are most vulnerable to attack. They will become alert and supplied with extra blood at the suggestion that an attack is to take place. The body's arousal system does not, of course, distinguish between a welcome attack and one which is unwelcome – that is the part which is all in the mind. Genital and other erogenous areas are aroused not only by expectations of sexual intercourse. It is well known that a man will always have an orgasm just before he is due to be hanged or otherwise executed. Female athletes experience nipple erection towards the conclusion of a competitive event. Cold weather makes nipples erect, as does any form of stimulation, whether it is mental, physical, sexual or non-sexual.

One researcher, Branko Bokun, a Yugoslav who has been studying for many years the effects of the mind on physical and mental illness, believes that what we have come to know as sexual arousal is actually increased stress located in the genital and breast areas. In an interesting and thought-provoking study, *Humour Therapy* (he is convinced that laughter is the best medicine and can cure many illnesses), Bokun describes what he believes to be the origin of sexual arousal and sexual desire. He says that humans have sexual fantasies when they are afraid and consumed by anxiety. Fear creates sexual arousal. This fear could be caused by expectation of a physical attack, or be created simply by fears and stresses which originate in the mind – fears of not being well liked, or of not being successful, or of not being able to cope in the adult world.

In the animal world, Bokun observes, sexual activity is always initiated by the female, during her mating season. He writes:

Stimulated through the senses and nervous system by external factors, usually light and temperature, the sex glands start releasing their hormones. This creates a sexual arousal, a biological discomfort, which is discharged by courting and mating.

In lower mammalians, mating is strictly conditioned by the female's readiness, by her seasonal fertility.

In animals, then, sexual arousal is a biological imperative, something which they cannot easily control. Humans, by contrast, says Bokun, play with their imaginations and create fantasies out of which sexual arousal emerges. As we know, the mind can create a complicated chain of hormonal activity throughout the body, causing physical discomfort and a variety of physical sensations, both pleasant and unpleasant.

According to Bokun:

Playing with our imagination can trigger off the hypothalamo-pituitary-gonadal system, bringing sexual arousal. The erotic reveries of a man can produce erection and readiness for copulation. The sexual fantasizing of a woman increases her vaginal flow and the pulsations of her clitoris.

He says that the areas we have come to know as erogenous are those which are most sensitive to any kind of arousal. The arousal is the same, he explains, whether the mind interprets this as fear, excitement, anxiety, terror or pleasure. The body knows only arousal, and it is the mind which makes the conclusions as to the source, according to what seems appropriate at the time. In the sexual sense, we usually interpret it as a lack if we do not feel 'turned on', or sexually aroused by somebody. Yet more often than not it is fear of one kind or another which creates the feeling of arousal and makes the erogenous zones activate.

The thought of spending a night with an illicit lover makes the heart beat faster and the sweat glands go into overproduction. We are excited, yes, but nervous at the same time. Yet if we are terrified of being raped or otherwise attacked, exactly the same physiological mechanisms would come into play. Many primates, Bokun tells us, have an erection when they are threatened, and often also when they are caught and put into captivity. Though there is arousal in the sexual areas, there is not a corresponding feeling of pleasure. The animal is simply terrified, and the body is gearing itself up for some sort of protective or defensive action. Fear of any kind stimulates the body's arousal system, and the first areas where this is noticed are the erogenous ones.

What we call sexual desire, according to Bokun, is actually fear. We are afraid of ourselves, of others, and we imagine we can dissipate these fears in sexual activity because we feel them in the sexual region. 'Why,' he asks, 'are we so obsessed with sex, persevering in this extra activity which is unnecessary for our survival, far beyond the needs of our species' reproduction, and which has now been proved to be the cause of cervical cancer and other diseases?'

He goes on:

An obsession with sex is basically a disease of the mind. . . . and it is the result of precariousness and restlessness, created by emotional arousal, originated by our conceited and pretentious minds.

That this obsession with sex is a disorder of the mind can be deduced from the fact that we are the only species to indulge in . . . oral and anal sex, that we have invented all manner of sexual cruelty and perversion, and that we practise sexual abuse of children.

The adolescent male, in Bokun's reckoning (and many men, he says, remain adolescent in outlook all their lives), feels the need to prove his validity with a success whenever his self-esteem and self-confidence are shaken. Sexual prowess is, for many men, the easiest sort to achieve. It demands no special intellectual skill, no long years of study, no special qualities of mind or character. Any man can become a sexual athlete, if he chooses, and sexual prowess is particularly appealing to the kind of man whose ego is built around conventional ideas of masculinity and virility. It is also easy to become a 'sexy' man, for it is possible to develop perpetual sexual readiness purely by using the mind to create fantasies. This is one reason why so many men like to look at pictures of naked or semi-naked women in seductive poses. It activates their fantasies, which they can then try to turn into reality, as a means of allaying deep-seated fears about themselves.

The body, of course, has to provide extra energy for the sexual activity which is inspired by the mind-created fantasies. The body mainly provides extra energy when it is frightened, and the mind supplies this fear, says Bokun, whenever its world develops doubts and its inflated ego is shaken.

'Most womanizers from Casanova to Don Juan to modern sexual maniacs are mainly insecure and fragile individuals in search of a boost to their egos. During revolutions and wars, when insecurity rules, sexual activity noticeably increases,' he writes.

We have ample evidence of this from stories of those who survived the horror of the concentration camps. Apparently, according to contemporary accounts, there was an immense amount of sexual activity going on among inmates, who spent almost the entire time in a state of practically unbelievable fear.

So what about women? Where do they fit into all this? As we have seen, many women never experience the slightest stirring of sexual desire, though all would have experienced arousal, which they may or may not have interpreted as sexual. Branko Bokun's explanation of the 'sex drive' in women is that in today's world women have adapted themselves to men and have found their best means of survival in being, or pretending to be, what is expected of them.

It is the normal practice in many cases that, even in sexual intercourse, the man does not try to satisfy his partner but only to fulfil his own ego. Often women guide men to reach satisfaction as quickly as possible, and are simply relieved when it is all over. Some even fake orgasms in order to boost their man's ego. In male-dominated cultures, women provide [sexual] services.

Where do women find the energy to behave in sexy ways? Bokun says that many women get this extra energy also from fear – from the fear of not being considered seductive, not being wanted, needed or desired, or are afraid of being lonely and helpless. It is not so much that women (or men) are motivated by pure, simple sexual hunger as that sex is regarded as a valid outlet for long-built-up fears and negative arousal states.

Most sexual intercourse, Bokun goes on, is simply the exploratory adventure of two self-loving people in search of exploitation of the other. Yet after they have had sexual intercourse, instead of feeling happier and more content, they feel even more lonely and frightened. This is because the physical sex has not achieved what it was meant to. It has not allayed the fears, because it is not capable of doing so. Sex is simply a physical act. We may invest it with all sorts of meanings, if we choose, but there is no way that a physical sensation could ever relieve the agonies of the mind. Those who try to blot out fears and worries by taking alcohol or drugs will know that, after a time, the problems will return to weigh upon them worse than before.

It is not so much that we humans are creatures who possess an insatiable sexual urge as that we are trying to use sex as a drug, an opiate. The more we attempt to satisfy sexual urges, the more restless and dissatisfied we will become as a result. We will wonder why sex has not relieved the burden but has made it worse. In our rage and disappointment, we will accuse the other person of not being sexy enough, not being loving or seductive or attractive or enough of a 'turn-on'. Yet this other person does not, or should not, exist simply to please us and to enable us to try to satisfy our ever more insatiable sexual appetite.

What most sex-manual writers have not realized is that

27

arousal is not a good thing. They spend pages and pages, often with extremely explicit diagrams, telling us how we can become aroused without ever acknowledging that arousal is simply an increase of stress in the body. We are aroused enough naturally by our ordinary lives, so why try to become aroused artificially? What good will it do?

The amount of stress that has been built up by the expectation of sex can, in part, be temporarily released by intercourse. But all that does is to prepare the way for more stress to build up. With any addiction, the appetite grows by what it feeds on – to paraphrase Shakespeare, who so thoroughly understood human psychology.

Dr David Lewis, a psychologist working at the University of Sussex, has researched the whole subject of arousal in relation to phobic and anxiety states. He has also discovered that, when the body is aroused, it does not and cannot distinguish between pleasure and pain, between pleasurable anticipation and terror, between anxiety and excitement. Part of his therapy for victims of phobias is to try to get them to 'reprogramme' their anxiety as excitement. A girl about to be raped would very probably experience intense arousal of all her erogenous zones, and this may make the rapist believe that she really 'wants it'. In romantic fiction the hero commonly says to the reluctant girl he is about to relieve of her virginity, 'Your body says yes.' But in such cases the erogenous areas are most probably being aroused by fear. We can, if we like, reprogramme this fear into pleasurable anticipation, but it remains a mental trick.

Branko Bokun writes:

When the sensitive parts of the body are caressed, gently massaged or kissed, our nervous system and body produce a special degree of emotional arousal which we translate into sexual excitement. Caressing and gentle massaging are all playful threats or mock attacks, which produce a range of special fears, or quasi-fears. The most erogenous parts of the body of an individual are usually also the most sensitive to real physical attacks.

Some biologists tell us that human sexual desire is biological urge, a natural imperative. But is it? If we look again at the animal world, we will find that sexual interest is present only so long as there are sex glands. When a cat has been 'neutered', it loses all interest in sexual activity. Humans, on the other hand, have come to believe that they must still have sexual feelings even if they have lost their sexual equipment. Women who undergo total hysterectomy are usually advised on how soon they can have sex again. But in these cases, when the reproductive equipment has vanished, where resides the seat of sexual desire? It cannot be in the ovaries – so it must be in the mind.

Most modern sex manuals say that any love relationship is made strong and secure by sexual fusion. Usually, this means only that, given time and persistence, a husband and wife – or other long-term partner – will be able to achieve orgasm together. In fact, reaching orgasm has become the main aim of many couples. But of course, no real relationship between two human beings can ever be based on a physical act. In time, inevitably, one partner will tire of the other, will find him or her less desirable, and will be tempted to go off in search of more exciting conquests. In itself, sex has no power either to fuse couples together or to drive them apart. It is only the mind's interpretation of this act, and its significance, which is important.

What we call being in love is actually a rite of passage, a movement from one lifestyle into another. People always and only ever fall in love when they are impatient with their present way of life and want to establish something dramatically different. Adolescents fall in love easily because they are breaking away from their parents, and attempting to establish independence. But of course, falling in love, like sex, is a complex emotional arousal which brings in its wake many physical changes such as high blood pressure, increased heart beat and reduced efficiency of the senses. When we are in love, our perceptions about the other person may be temporarily dimmed. This is the traditional 'love is blind' idea.

When people are first in love, they long to possess the other entirely, and may become extremely jealous even when there is no cause or justification. They also become irritable and insecure, because they are afraid of losing this other person. This fear can make lovers engage in ferocious sexual activity, as a way of gluing the relationship together. Both partners mistakenly imagine that sex will fuse them together, deepen their love. In fact, it does not have this power.

Far from being 'natural' and healthy, sex is actually a condition of high emotional and physical arousal which affects many bodily functions, usually to their detriment. When the body is in a state of heightened arousal its immune function is damped down and its resistance to illness decreases. Also, sex can cause forms of mental disorder, such as selfishness, self-centredness and conceit.

Yet, in the face of all the evidence, the myth persists that sex is good for us and that in order to be happy and fulfilled as individuals we need more and more. My own belief, which I shall explore in detail through this book, is that it is celibacy, rather than sex, which is the natural state for humans. What we interpret as 'sexual desire' is merely over-arousal, caused by fears and anxieties which have nothing whatever to do with a biological imperative. It is not the over-activity of the sex organs which gives rise to sexual desire, but feelings of fear, dependence, ego and all the other jumble of emotions we experience as humans. These we may collectively label sexual frustration which we imagine will go away if only we can experience transcendental sex. Of course, as we all know, the frustration remains.

For a woman, however one likes to look at it, sexual intercourse constitutes a form of attack. It may be a welcome attack, or it may be unwelcome, according to who is at the end of the erect organ. Mentally, the woman may have longed for the sex act to take place, but still the *body* will recognize the act as an attack and react accordingly. What is usually interpreted as satisfied desire is actually relief – in physiological terms – that it is over. The body can now relax: the attack is finished.

To sum up, we do not, as a species, 'need' sex in the same way we need food, drink and sleep – and we can live quite well without it if we so choose. There is no biological foundation whatever for the belief that sexual energies will, if not used in the proper way, turn in on themselves and wreak mental and physical havoc and restlessness. There is also no evidence at all for the idea that there is a biochemical urge which builds up and which has to be released at intervals, to maintain health. Marie Stopes believed this, but she was wrong.

In our society it has become a form of boasting for a man or woman to profess that he or she needs lots of sex, and elderly people who imply they are still having sexual relations tend to be admired. We laugh at Australian monstrosity Dame Edna Everage talking on television about the fact she still has 'drives and juices' – but we all feel we should continue to have these drives, whatever our age and condition.

When an individual is celibate from choice – and not because it seems impossible to find a partner – a calmer and more contented condition is automatically created in the body. The body actually prefers the state of celibacy to that of a sexually active existence with its continuous hormonal upheaval and fluctuation. The system is designed to perform in a calm manner, and not to be continuously over-aroused. The arousal mechanism is there for our protection to be used only occasionally, when needed.

Sex manuals commonly state that sexual activity gives individuals extra energy. In fact, nothing could be further from the truth, as anybody conversant with the second law of thermodynamics will be aware. This law, which states that energy cannot be created or destroyed, but only transferred, has come to be accepted as being as universally true as the law of gravity. If we use up energy for one activity, of necessity this will be displaced from another pursuit. The best course of action is to use energies wisely and to conserve what energy we have for worthwhile activities. Those who dissipate their energies in sexual thought and activity risk adversely affecting other areas of their lives. Sex – apart from its essential purpose of reproduction – is ultimately an unproductive and time-wasting activity. It does not add to the sum of human happiness but rather takes happiness away. I shall try to show why I believe this in the chapters that follow.

CHAPTER 2

Celibacy and tradition – a short review

In almost every age apart from our own, celibacy has been held in high regard – as a more elevated ideal, usually, than the married or non-celibate state.

By contrast, those people who sold their bodies for sex as prostitutes have been universally despised throughout history. They have been regarded as shameful, low-grade people for resorting to such a way of life. Even in our own age, in which celibacy has long ceased to be an ideal, we still retain a low opinion of prostitutes.

Just about every religion and philosophical system, at least until modern times, has agonized over the question of sexual intercourse and whether it is a right or wrong activity. Philosophers have argued over whether sex can make a man better or worse, whether it can elevate or debase him. In ancient times, of course, nobody worried very much about what women thought in the matter. Women counted for little, as many early philosophers – Plato included – believed that a punishment for men who had misbehaved in this life was to return to earth in the next as a woman. Hindu doctrine still adheres to this belief that it is 'lower' to be a woman than to be a man.

In ancient times, women were not supposed to have fleshly desires and temptations of their own. They were either chaste, or dedicated to tempting men away from the straight and narrow. Plato, for example, described his ideal woman as being simple, obedient and affectionate – rather like a household pet. Plato had no conception of a woman being as intelligent, or having thought processes as complicated as those of a man. Nor was she as sensitive, or as capable of abstract thought. She was, in fact, little higher than an animal.

Women were then seen largely in relation to men and were not regarded as people who existed independently. One reason for this may be that as most major philosophies and religions were devised by men for men, they spoke only to their own kind. Yet all philosophers and founders of religions fundamentally recognized that women had the power to bring a man down to earth and remind him that he had a body after all. That was why women had to be segregated and secluded – they could tempt men beyond endurance. It was all, of course, the woman's fault if a man did succumb.

In his *History of Western Philosophy*, Bertrand Russell gives us a potted version of Plato's theory of immortality. The body, according to Plato, brings us in touch with the world of external reality, but it is evil and a source of lusts. It is lust, says Plato, which causes all violence and all war. Only by getting rid of the foolishness of the body can we become pure. True philosophers are those people who are able to abstain totally from fleshly lusts. Plato declares: 'Each pleasure and pain is a sort of nail which nails and rivets the soul to the body, until she [the soul] becomes like the body and believes to be true what the body affirms to be true.'

After Plato, another Greek philosopher, Epicurus, states: 'Sexual intercourse has never done a man good and he is lucky if it has not harmed him.' According to Epicurus, founder of the philosophical school usually known as the Epicureans, the safest form of social pleasure is friendship, which does not make these bodily demands and does not lead to lust, which, like Plato, he saw as evil.

Of course, praise of celibacy goes back much further than the ancient Greeks. From the very earliest times, Eastern spiritual traditions have elevated celibacy above marriage. The Sanskrit word for celibacy, *brahmacharya*, is also the word for student. Hindu tradition says that a man (again, women are not thought worthy of special mention, and are excluded from philosophical aspirations) should ideally pass through four states in his life. After childhood, he becomes *brahmacharya*, a student. It was held impossible to combine intellectual study with sexual activity – an idea to which we certainly no longer subscribe. If energies were being put into the sexual act, it was maintained, they could not at the same time be put into intellectual pursuits. One cancelled out the other.

After the student stage – at about 25 years of age – the man entered the next stage of his life and became a *garhasthya*, or householder. During these years he married and raised a family. That phase being over, both married partners should consider becoming *vanaprastha*, or recluses, abstaining from sex, as it would no longer be appropriate to their more dignified condition. I understand that to this day married couples in India would regard it as most bizarre to carry on sexual activity after their children were grown up. Very often, the signal to stop having sex is when the eldest child becomes a parent.

In Hindu tradition, the last state is of the *sannyas*, who is entirely alone and shakes of all worldly ties to meditate and become holy. In present-day India it is still considered admirable for an older man to leave his wife and family, wear saffron robes and live in a cave, alone. There would again, at this stage, be no thought whatever of physical sex, as the man's entire thought would be occupied with purely spiritual contemplation and meditation.

Many, though not all, of the major world religions advocate that celibacy is essential if one is to pursue a spiritual path. The ancient Romans, who were not noticeably celibate, still had their Vestal Virgins, whose power came from the very fact that they never engaged in sexual intercourse. In fact, if any did the punishment was death. Lack of virginity would instantly cause them to lose their spiritual power.

There were in all six priestesses of the goddess Vesta whose job was to guard the sacred fire in her temple at Rome. The Virgins were chosen by lot from twenty maidens of high parentage and they officiated for at least thirty years. Ten of these were spent learning, ten in administering the rites and another ten in teaching the newcomers. In ancient Greece, female soothsayers had to be celibate, otherwise they would lose their powers.

For many hundreds of years, the idea persisted that things spiritual and intellectual did not go together with those of the body. Those who were interested and preoccupied with satisfying bodily desires could not at the same time pursue matters of the spirit. Rigorous separation from earthly and heavenly pursuits was needed.

Bodily lusts, according to ancient tradition, dragged a man down rather than lifting him up.

Buddhism, an ancient faith that in recent years has been attracting a growing number of adherents in the West, also has a long tradition of celibacy for its priests and monks. Many Buddhists in the East are expected to spend a period of time as a celibate monk in a monastery. Even Thailand, in many ways an extremely secular country, adheres to this tradition and its men are all expected to enter a monastery at some stage. Bhumiphol, the King of Thailand, has spent time in a monastery. Like many ancient religious practices, the tradition applies to men only.

The Jewish religion is one of the few ancient systems which does not have a tradition of celibacy for its priests (rabbis), but in pre-Christian times the Essenes were a community of celibates who felt that in order to pursue holiness abstention from sex was essential.

By the time we come to the Christian era, we find that the question of celibacy has become confused. Jesus himself was, as we know, perpetually celibate, as was his mother, but he himself did not talk much about whether celibacy or marriage was the higher path. We know that he befriended prostitutes and others cast out from decent society, but it was left to St Paul to pronounce categorically on chastity for Christians. Usually regarded as a misogynist, Paul said that it was better to marry than to burn – that is, with lust – and that if a man could not contain himself, he had better get married. Again, no consideration is given to what women might feel about it all.

It was the early Christian saints – Jerome, Benedict and Augustine – who established finally the idea that the priesthood should be celibate for life. All three wrote about the terrible struggles they personally experienced in following chastity and how difficult they found it to overcome the lusts of the flesh. St Benedict, by all accounts, had to resort to acts of extreme masochism in order to achieve his spiritual goal. Apparently, while in the desert, he was so disturbed by visions of dancing maidens that he had to strip off and throw himself in a bush of thorns, there to thrash around until the pain had excised all his sexual desires. Thus Benedict established the idea, which has persisted to our own day, that extreme asceticism and purging of the flesh was necessary in order to remain continent.

In some ways, the insistence of the early Christian fathers on celibacy was a reaction to the sexual excesses of the later days of the Roman Empire. The very asceticism of Christianity was, in its early days, a potent attraction for those who were wearied and sated by Roman licence. During the third and fourth centuries early Christians extolled sexual continence as a permanent state, but they did recognize that this was a condition not all could achieve.

While St Paul allowed that husbands and wives should give themselves bodily to each other, except at certain times which would be devoted to prayer, St Augustine viewed the very act of sexual intercourse as inherently disgusting. A later Christian apologist, Arnobius, called the act filthy and degrading and was of the opinion that God should have invented a better, cleaner way of propagating the species.

In the writings of Augustine, we find that this saint believed that both men and women were originally creatures of the mind and spirit, with no carnal desires at all. The earliest humans, he believed, would have been in complete control of their bodies, uninterested in anything erotic or physically arousing. The idea of fulfilling sexual desires would have been quite alien to them. In the past golden age, he maintained, men and women would have had no carnal desire for each other, but would have participated in intercourse as animals do, purely for the purposes of reproduction. As Christian doctrines gradually hardened into an inviolable belief system, intercourse became connected with original sin, and only those who were celibate, it was said, could hope to achieve eternal blessings. For a long time, the idea persisted in Christianity that sex without passion was morally preferable to sex with passion. This was an idea that came originally from Plato, who held that 'absent-minded' sex and reproduction would not be damaging to the true philosopher. It was only when passions were engaged that the pursuit became dangerous and detracted from pleasures of the mind, which were always seen as greater and more lasting than those of the senses.

Of course, by no means all early Christian saints were male. Most of the female saints whose names we remember were virgins and many suffered appalling persecution because of this. They became saints because they decided they would rather suffer torture than relinquish their virginity. The idea grew up that virginity somehow protected a woman and made her inviolable – not only to men, but also to flames, racks and other forms of torture. The first-century saint Thecla, for example, who heard St Paul preaching and immediately decided to become converted to his doctrines, remained a virgin all her life. She had been engaged to marry, but broke off the engagement and dedicated herself to a life of Christianity and virginity. Naturally enough, men were outraged by this decision of hers, and tried to destroy her. Yet her virginity protected her from wild beasts, and from flames, and meant that she could not die.

Thecla's story, found in an apocryphal second-century document, *The Acts of Paul*, makes fascinating if rather incredible reading. The document attributed many miracles to the first Christian saint, and was a bestseller for a couple of centuries. In Christianity, unlike many of the more ancient traditions, women as well as men could attain to a state of grace if they kept themselves celibate.

The virgin was more powerful than the married woman because she remained independent of men, looking only to God, a non-material entity, for her sustenance. In an interesting article in *The Guardian* on St Thecla, the writer Karen Armstrong, a former nun, postulates that in the stories of these early female saints we can find the seeds of modern feminism. When she was a fiancée, thinking about getting married, Thecla was entirely dependent on men and saw herself as living through them. Once she vowed perpetual virginity, she achieved independence and power, which were strong enough to enable her to stand up to the most ferocious and sadistic men of her day. (The best-known example of a female saint achieving power through continued virginity is of course Joan of Arc.)

Thecla's virginity, writes Karen Armstrong, brought

about freedom from male domination and enabled her to become a Christian apostle in her own right. As she was impregnable by men, so she achieved autonomy and preserved her powers. In later life she became a great healer and miracle-worker. Men continued to be outraged by her, and even when she was 90 years old tried to rape her so that she would lose her miraculous powers. Needless to say, they did not succeed.

As Christianity spread, so did the idea that love between man and woman could actually lead to spiritual love. This was the tradition of courtly love, whereby the knight courting his ever-unattainable lady was eventually led to love of God. Loving his lady was a learning process. In the poems of John Donne, we can see a gradual progression from love of a woman to love of God.

The Puritans, of course, believed that voluntary celibacy was all but impossible, and that sexual urges had to be rigorously repressed. Our own secular age has come to regard those adhering to religious beliefs as anti life, anti-the senses, and anti passion and excitement.

As Christianity declined and became degraded, the idea that sex was inherently sinful became increasingly open to question. Celibate Catholic priests are no longer, in the main, seen as repositories of wisdom, or more spiritual than those who have embraced the married state. In fact, we have come to believe the complete opposite – that a man or woman who is celibate is only half a person and, in abstaining from sex, is not qualified to pronounce on any area of life whatever. Indeed, celibacy is now seen as taking away from, rather than conferring, wisdom. Many people are now virtually affronted by the idea of the perpetual celibate, whom they regard as somebody who knows nothing about love between human beings or about family life, presuming to advise on relationships, birth control, or indeed any other aspect of life.

There are now very definite moves to abolish the celibate priesthood in the Catholic Church, as celibacy is now seen as an incomplete state. Pressure groups are compaigning for Catholic priests to be allowed to marry and carry on their work as before. Margaret Evening, a Christian and author of *Who Walk Alone*, a book which attempts to explain the purpose of the single state, claims:

'It is nonsense to think that he [the priest] cannot understand men because he does not live like them. It is not
necessary to have experienced all human situations in
order to be guided by the Holy Spirit in the direction of
souls.'

She continues:

Chastity does not consist of deadening our heart, but rather in
giving it a liberty of love, a single aim, a transparency to God.
Our chastity indeed, our whole life, only makes sense in
relation to love of God. Should not chastity be a dynamic way of
witness in this present age of permissiveness and sex obsession? As I have understood it, it never was prudery, nor a cold
negation of our humanity, a maiming of life . . . Chastity is not
meant to stunt our personality.

In our present age, celibacy has greatly suffered by
being closely associated with the pursuit of a religious
vocation. Most of us, nowadays, do not want to have
anything to do with organized religion, and wish to
dissociate ourselves in the widest possible way from it.
This means not adhering to any of the precepts that have
been handed down by these religions. Today we feel we
know better, and that the religious people of the past were
cold-hearted, puritanical bigots who were, in Freudian
terms, sublimating their sex drives and allowing them to
go underground rather than emerge in a healthy and
natural way. In our attempts to overthrow the hold
religion has on us, we have deliberately attempted to do
the opposite from the doctrines it preaches.

One of the major reasons why celibacy has fallen into
disrepute during this century is that it has been seen in
conjunction only with organized religion, and 'thou shalt
not'. In our age, religion has been regarded as a repressive
system which casts cold, disapproving glances at anything we might want to enjoy. Celibacy, in being associated with religion, has been viewed mainly in negative
terms, as self-denial, rather than as a potent means of
achieving freedom and independence. In our own day,
those who have voluntarily embraced celibacy are usually
regarded as religious extremists and, because of this, very
strange and possibly rather dangerous.

If we want to look at the good side of celibacy we need

to separate it from religion, or at least from the currently degraded state of most religions. Instead of dismissing celibacy as a repressive religious doctrine, we need to ask ourselves *why* it was that so many ancient moral codes and philosophers held sexual intercourse to be essentially wrong – certainly if it were done with passion, and as a means of gratifying the senses, rather than for the purposes of reproduction.

As so many of these old religions advocated sexual abstinence, we ought at least to consider the possibility that they were offering some sort of wisdom, something which was to some degree a part of universal truth. Old religions maintained that celibacy was essential if one wanted to establish a proper connection with God. One could not, it was maintained, be connecting with God at the same time as connecting with a human being.

In our own day, we have come to see sex itself as sublime, almost as a religious experience in its own right, and we have not been interested in celibacy – partly because, in the main, we do not want to connect ourselves with God. The majority of Westerners do not, nowadays, believe in the existence of God anyway, so why should we attempt to connect ourselves to someone or something which is simply a figment of the imagination? In the case of another human being, you know he or she is real, that the person exists. Why forgo sensual pleasures for he purposes of establishing some sort of relationship with such a nebulous concept?

There is also the fact that most of us do not like God as he has been portrayed through standard Christian teachings. To feminists, the Christian god – man in his own image – seems to be simply part of the patriarchal system; and to non-Christians, God seems intent on saying that anything we enjoy is automatically sinful and wicked. Because we have largely rejected the idea of a Christian god, we have at the same time rejected the wisdom that was originally contained in religious doctrines. We have thrown the baby out with the bathwater, as it were.

I am not a religious person and I do not adhere to any particular set of religious beliefs, so I shall try to explain why I believe celibacy is at the root of many religious systems. I regard 'God' not as an old man sitting up above with a white beard passing judgement and sending us all to heaven or hell, but as the ultimate aspiration of all human beings – the ideal, if you like, the perfect individual who possesses only virtues and is totally without vices.

If we ourselves want to become 'better' human beings and more like God, we need to use our brains and intellect rather than our non-intellectual senses. When sex is described as 'animal passion' this does not mean that in having frequent sex we are acting like animals, who patently do not have sex all that often. What it means is that, instead of using our intellectual powers, we are attempting to gratify physical senses, and doing this does not enable us to learn or understand anything, either about ourselves or about the world around us. Sensual pleasures serve to blunt, rather than sharpen, the intellect.

The ancients understood that the more time you are able to devote to study, contemplation, reading and learning, the less energy or inclination you will have for sex. It is not that you give it up so much as that it ceases to become important in your life. The teaching of the old religions is that, in order to become a better, purer human being it is essential to spend time in study and prayer. Only in these quiet times can creative energies be released and true individuality realized; only by having time to oneself can you realize your true potential. Virginia Woolf realized the importance of having time to oneself when she wrote that a woman has to have 'a room of her own' in order to become a creative artist.

Today, the idea that people can become better or more creative by cutting themselves off from lust and greed is laughed at and derided. One is accused of having one's head in the clouds and being unrealistic. One of the reasons for this is, I am sure, that many of those who set themselves up as religious advisers – priests, vicars, rabbis – do not even begin to set a good example of how to live. Vicars in the Church of England have mistresses, get divorced, chase after choirboys and otherwise lead lives very far removed from celibacy or near-celibacy. Many Catholic priests have left their vocation in order to marry or set up home with a woman with whom they have fallen in love. If professedly religious people cannot follow celibacy, we ask, can there be any real point in even trying ourselves?

If celibacy is to be seen today as a worthwhile idea in itself, it has to be separated from religion. I prefer to view celibacy as a way of finding one's true self, of asserting one's own individuality, having personal power – not over other people, but over oneself; to be someone 'whose passions not his masters are', as the old hymn has it. If celibacy is embraced for the right reasons, it confers personal power, grace, autonomy and independence. If it is simply seen as an exercise in self-denial and self-mastery, or as a way of withdrawing from human contact, then it can be a negative condition. It is not that one tries and tries to overcome fleshly lusts and keeps failing and then berating oneself for being wicked, but that, in establishing personal autonomy, the need for bodily interaction with another person begins to recede of its own accord. In describing the torments they endured in trying to overcome physical passion, those early Christian saints have a lot to answer for.

In our own age, almost the only people willingly embracing prolonged celibacy – apart from some exceptionally creative and special individuals – are those who are usually thought of as religious nuts. Mormons, the most familiar examples of which are those impossibly clean-looking young men who knock at doors and offer to explain their faith to those who do not want to hear about it, take a vow of chastity before marriage and even wear a special all-in-one undergarment to prevent sexual feelings.

Many of those who follow Eastern religions and movements (for example, the Hare Krishnas who chant their way down Oxford Street dressed in saffron robes) are also celibate if unmarried. The fact that the only people – as it seems – extolling celibacy are those who belong to minority cults has made us view abstinence from sex as a minority pursuit. In fact, all ancient systems of belief, whether or not celibacy was part of the religion, laid down very stringent rules for sexual intercourse. In the Old Testament, instructions to the Levites stipulated specific times at which sex was permitted – and those times were when the woman was most likely to conceive.

While Orthodox Jews still follow these teachings, they are disregarded by the majority of Jews. Today, by contrast, we have come to believe that sex should happen all the time, and have landed ourselves in a peculiar set of problems because of this belief.

CHAPTER 3

Celibacy and health

The current orthodoxy states that sex is good for you. For very many years now, we have heard that it is important, even essential, to satisfy the sexual urge regularly. We humans are all sexual beings, we have been told; we all have sexual equipment, and why is it there unless it is meant to be used?

Since the popular wisdom says that we are all sexual beings, it is assumed that there is actually something wrong with those who are not interested in, or say they do not enjoy, sex. 'Loss of libido' has come to be seen as an actual medical condition, one which doctors attempt to treat with drugs or other forms of therapy. Indeed, many hospitals now run sexual dysfunction clinics where people can go if they feel they are suffering from impotence, vaginismus or frigidity. The amount of libido a person has is now often taken as an indicator of good health generally. Cardiologists commonly view a renewed interest in sex as a sign that their heart patients are definitely getting better. Relatives of desperately ill people suffering from all kinds of conditions may be told by the doctor, with a twinkle in his eye: 'He must be getting better – he was chatting up one of the nurses today.'

Good health has now become equated with a lusty, that is, sexy, attitude towards life. If you are still interested in sex, patients are often told by their doctors, there cannot be very much wrong with you.

In the previous chapter I said that I believed it is celibacy, rather than sex, which is good for you, for celibacy creates a condition of calmness and peace in the body which is essential for continuing good health. I shall try to explain further in this chapter why I think it is celibacy, rather than sex, which enhances health.

I have come to believe that sex is, or can be, actually bad for your health. I am not referring in this respect only to the specifically sex-related diseases, though these do present an ever-growing and intractable problem, but conditions which seem to have little obvious connection with the sexual act, such as high blood pressure and heart disease.

In fact, though very many doctors have extolled the virtues of sex, and have written large numbers of books devoted to sexual technique and sexual satisfaction, there is a growing body of scientific evidence which says that abstinence from sex can actually confer glowing, lasting health.

I have combed diligently through medical and scientific literature and can find no evidence whatever that abstinence from sex, for however long, has any detrimental effect on health. Lifelong celibates do not die earlier, nor do they succumb to mysterious disorders which could be corrected by sexual intercourse. In fact, looking purely at the medical evidence, it seems that the reverse is true. Studies of nuns and monks – the only groups of people who are celibate for a lifetime – have shown that these people tend to be far healthier in every way than those having regular sex.

A large-scale study of over 2,000 nuns, undertaken in 1968, showed that they succumbed far less to blood-pressure problems than a group of non-celibate women doing exactly the same jobs. Both the nuns and the married women had jobs as teachers, nurses or social workers. The researchers had no choice but to conclude – reluctantly – that celibacy must be a factor in the better all-round general health of the nuns.

The disorder most people worry about nowadays is that which is somewhat vaguely termed 'stress'. The term, originally coined by the late Hans Selye, who pioneered work on this disorder, came from the engineering world. All engineers are familiar with metal stress and metal fatigue. Selye defined stress as 'the body's non-specific response to any demand placed upon it, whether unpleasant or pleasant.'

None of us can live without stress of some kind. It is undue stress which creates health problems, and which sets up imbalances in the body. Traditionally, it has been thought that sex has the power to relieve pent-up stress and that it can, by so doing, help people to carry on more effectively with their daily lives. Sex, we have come to believe, can be a potent means of relaxing and unwinding. It can be rather like a stiff brandy, only better, because at the same time as you are releasing all your frustrations and bottled-up feelings, you are experiencing transcendent bliss with the one you love. That, at any rate, is the theory, though few experience such utter relaxation in real life.

Mahatma Gandhi, one of the most famous of modern celibates, who took a vow of lifelong *brahmacharya* when he was 36, wrote:

It has not been proved to my satisfaction that sexual union in marriage is itself good and beneficial to the unionists ... momentary excitement and satisfaction there certainly was. But it was invariably followed by exhaustion. And the desire for union returned immediately the effect of exhaustion wore out. Although I have always been a conscientious worker, I can clearly recall that this indulgence interfered with my work. It was the consciousness of this limitation that put me on the track of self-restraint and I have no manner of doubt that the self-restraint is responsible for the comparative freedom from illness that I have enjoyed for long periods, and for my output of energy and work both physical and mental which eyewitnesses have described as phenomenal.

One of the reasons Gandhi could work so long and hard was that the energy he might have put into sex – and the stress which would accompany the desire and expectation of the physical act – could be channelled into pursuits which, for him, were more worthwhile. Also, his body was not subject to the hormonal fluctuations associated with the sex act and the feelings which go with physical intercourse. It is not possible to have sexual intercourse devoid of emotions – even though, as we have seen, ancient philosophers recommended this as an ideal. For though it might be possible for one partner to engage in sex 'absent-mindedly', as Plato put it, the other partner might not see it that way.

The fantasy that one experiences almost spiritual bliss when in the arms of a loved one, and during and after sex is, unfortunately, just that: a fantasy. The fantasy has fed a thousand romantic novels and films, but if it were a reality we would not need to have the fantasy. After all, everybody knows that physical appetite for food is satisfied by eating, so we do not have to read books and see films which show us that this is the case. But when we hear how sexual hunger can be assuaged by intercourse, then we listen, and read. *We pay attention not because we know it is true, but because we would like it to be.*

Emotional yearnings, which are often described as sexual, can never be satisfied by another person, and the expectation, belief or hope that they can be will lead to further frustration, stress and discontent. When was a lover ever satisfied? He spends a longed-for night with his mistress and before he knows where he is he wants to do it again. 'Satisfaction' through physical sex is simply not possible. All that happens is that the desire for more is created, along with increased stress.

Those who lead celibate lives are often asked whether or not they miss sex and whether they find they have to masturbate when the urge becomes unbearable. When they answer with perfect truth that they never experience a desire for sex, they are simply not believed.

New scientific evidence is now emerging concerning the nature of arousal hormones and how they affect the body. They can provide an explanation as to how sex, in the broadest sense of the word, constitutes a definite danger to health. When the sympathetic nervous system, which is responsible for gearing the body into high arousal states, receives messages from the brain to move into some sort of action, body chemicals such as adrenalin are released in large quantities. Once adrenalin is flowing in the body, it becomes difficult not to act. The whole system is geared up and must somehow have an outlet. Expectation of the sexual act can turn on this arousal system in a powerful way. When the sex act has been completed and orgasm occurs, a feedback circuit back to the brain says that the mission is now accomplished and the task finished. The mind interprets orgasm as pleasurable relief, and so the arousal system switches itself off. So far, so good, This is what happens when 'desire' is satisfied. While the non-arousal system – known technically as the parasympathetic nervous system – comes into play, the feeling experienced is one of restoration and relaxation. But after a time the arousal hormones start circulating again of their own accord and the familiar feeling of tension starts up again. The more sex you have, the more the body's chemicals become geared up to expect it. After a time, the system is hardly ever in a calm state, but is continuously being aroused, though by no means is it always satisfied.

People who are in the habit of having extremely regular sex will find themselves being aroused by sexual images, such as pictures of half-naked women in newspapers, semi-pornographic posters on the Underground or blatantly pornographic pictures in men's magazines. When in a constant state of sexual arousal, anything even moderately suggestive can act as a powerful trigger for the sex hormones and also adrenalin to start coursing around the body again.

The trouble is that there is no way of satisfying the sexual urge every time it manifests itself. Doctors often advise those troubled by sexual feelings for which they seem to have no outlet to masturbate to relieve the tension. Although this can achieve its purpose in the short term, it just keeps the sexual tension alive. It is a bit like taking saccharin when trying to give up sugar or methadone to conquer a heroin habit – all you are doing is keeping the sweet tooth or drug addiction alive.

There is no way anybody can ever have 'enough' sex because every sexual act will keep these arousal hormones in motion. But – and this is the really stressful, frustrating, health-destroying aspect of sex – there is no end product, no achievement. Leaving aside for the moment the question of pregnancy, the possibility of starting a future life, sex is ultimately a sterile activity. Nothing happens once you have done it. The desire which is itself engendered by sex is momentarily set at ease by sex but this in itself sets up the need for more. It is like going round in ever-decreasing circles. You never break outside the circle, and never achieve true freedom – independence from sex. Sex patently does not make you happier, more powerful, more intelligent, or a better, more warm-hearted person. If it did, everybody in the world would be these things. All it can achieve is the need for more sex.

And that, of course, can directly have adverse health consequences.

The nature of sexual desire was discussed at length in Chapter One; this chapter is concerned simply with the health aspects. Its basic effect on health is to increase the amount of stress undergone by the body's systems. I am not speaking here only of the specifically sexual areas, but of the entire system. When we want sex but cannot have it, we commonly describe this as frustration. This frustration is perceived in the body as stress, not just sexual stress, but generalized stress.

Whatever kind of stress a person is under, and whether this comes from having problems at work, trying to look after small children or having an elderly relative in the house, the same mechanisms come into play. The body does not differentiate between sexual and other kinds of stress. It simply means that the system is constantly geared for action that is by no means always going to take place.

When the system is perpetually under heightened arousal, the body's defences are reduced and the ability to cope with all kinds of illness, even coughs and colds, is lessened.

Apart from specifically sex-related diseases, there is another insidious way in which sex can be detrimental to health. Very many people see sex as a way of dealing with their problems. This was briefly touched on in Chapter One. Those who have difficulties at work or at home are very often advised to seek solace in a satisfying sexual relationship with a close partner. Sex is very often – perhaps most often – used as a way of coping with deep-seated personal problems, and of drowning sorrows. It can be used as a kind of emotional Sellotape or sticking plaster, a way of patching up quarrels between couples. But when sex is used as a means of settling differences, all that is really happening is that the cracks are being papered over. Underneath, they are getting larger all the time.

Using sex to overcome problems is very much like using chemical tranquillizers, which we have now come to view as a disastrous way of coping with emotional difficulties. Yet for years they were hailed as a miracle cure, a non-addictive, easy way of relieving stress. When a person takes benzodiazepine tranquillizers, all troubles and worries appear to fade away and a calm state ensues – for as long as he or she is taking the pills. But once the tablets are withdrawn for any reason, or become un-obtainable, the individual finds that his or her innate coping mechanisms have completely disappeared. Not only that, but all the old worries are still there – they have been bottled up inside, and prevented from coming to the surface so that they can be expelled from the system.

Exactly the same happens with sex. The only difference is that with sexual intercourse the tranquillizer comes from inside, rather than having been manufactured in a laboratory. When sex is used as a means of coping with problems, the hypothalamus – the gland situated in the brain which controls reason and emotions – becomes fooled into thinking that the problems have actually been solved. The truth is that they are still there and are getting deeper and more difficult to solve all the time. This can have important consequences for mental, and eventually physical, health, as the two are inextricably linked.

When a couple enters into a sexual relationship and it eventually comes to an end, they very often turn against each other, and start to hate each other. Hate takes the place of what used to be considered love. So many divorced couples, who have been in a sexual relationship for years, simply never speak to each other again when the decree absolute comes through. For many years they may have tried to solve their differences through sex, only to find that once the sexual aspect ceases there is a yawning, unbridgeable chasm over which they can no longer communicate at all.

In nature, humans are the only animals that indulge in sex for purely recreational purposes. Animals think about sex only when there is the possibility of an end result – the likelihood of reproduction. Though some animals do form close ties with each other and become 'friends', this bond is never, ever based upon sex. But there is also evidence that animals too can benefit from a celibate life. In one study, two groups of laboratory rats were treated identically as regards food and living conditions, but one group was kept celibate while the others were allowed an ordinary sex life. It was found that the celibate group lived far longer, and also kept much healthier, possibly because of the lack of fluctuation in arousal hormones.

According to researches carried out by those well-known American sexologists Kinsey, Masters and Johnson, men do not suffer any physical ill effects from not having sex, though mentally they may perceive a sexless life as a deprivation. Women too, can live completely sexless lives without ill effects. But when there is a *perception* that not all is well, there may well be health problems. In her book *Married Love*, Marie Stopes wrote that many women were prone to hysteria and fainting fits because they suffered from sexual repression, and were distressed by the idea that it was wrong for 'nice' women to feel carnal desire. Her book is an impassioned plea for women to understand the nature of the sexual urge and to give expression to it. It is certainly true that any kind of repression is bad for people. While we continue to persist in regarding ourselves primarily as sexual creatures we will continue to feel repressed, frustrated and unfulfilled – however much sex we may be having. The sexual urge is eternally unsatisfied because it is unsatisfiable, and no amount of releasing of inhibitions will ever overcome that. Marie Stopes, it will be remembered, had been married for several years before she realized that there might be something wrong with her own sex life. In fact her marriage was unconsummated and was later annulled.

Her books have to be read in the light of this personal fact. She felt cheated, once she realized what had happened, and thereafter decided to dedicate her life to promoting free expression of the sex act – but without the unfortunate consequences of children, unless they were wanted.

Because sex is such a highly arousing biochemical activity, it brings other very strong emotions to the surface. Most of these are negative and can therefore lead to health problems. Anybody who perceives that sex should play an important part in his or her life is liable to feel, at times, jealousy, anger, greed, lust and hate – all the emotions that have, in fact, been associated with the onset of serious illness. We are so used to feeling angry, hurt, jealous and so on – whether or not these feelings have anything to do with sex – that we have come to regard these emotions as normal, but in fact the body does not welcome these states of increased arousal; it thrives instead on the positive emotions of love, contentment, inner peace and the consciousness of wanting to give, rather than take.

In recent years it has been assumed that there is a level of sexual desire which we must all feel, and that anything above or below this line is abnormal and constitutes a medical problem. Lack of desire for physical sex is something that bothers many doctors, as their patients are always coming to them saying they no longer fancy the wife or husband: could there be something wrong with them? Can the doctor 'give them something' for it?

'We all have a sex drive of some kind,' allege doctors Andrew and Penny Stanway, and Philip Cauthery, in their book *The Complete Book of Love and Sex*. They then spend the rest of the book's 448 pages telling us ignorant non-medical people how to get the very best out of sexual relationships. I am sure they mean no harm, but by what divine right do they imagine they may tell the rest of us how to run our lives? Sex, like so many other aspects of our lives, has now become a medical matter, with doctors acting as the experts, or sexperts. The doctors claim in their 'complete' book that if older men are not in regular contact with women their interest in sex will slowly decline. Instead of accepting this as normal and natural and to be seen as a welcome relief, the doctors then go on to suggest that the 'sex lives of older couples can be enhanced by sex aids'. They also state that many women lose interest in sex after the menopause. Again, there is no thought of allowing sex interest to fade away gradually. Instead, according to the book, an interest in sex has to be artificially renewed, or 'treated', sometimes by giving the woman male hormone. It is as if nobody is *allowed* to be unsexual nowadays.

As we are now supposed to be sexual beings all our lives – why, one cannot even begin to imagine – a whole industry has grown up on the premise that those people who have sexual 'problems' must be 'treated'. David Delvin, another doctor who has become one of our favourite sexperts, observed in a medical journal that most surgeries are inundated with patients who feel they have sexual difficulties. Almost 60 per cent of adults aged 25 or over experience some kind of sexual difficulty at some time, according to Dr Delvin. For most men, the main problem is impotence, caused usually by depression or anxiety rather than actual physical incapacity. For women, the commonest problem is vaginismus, or a tightening of the pelvis and other muscles at the mere prospect of sex. A very common problem for men is premature ejaculation (who decides what is premature, I wonder?). This, according to Masters and Johnson, can be treated by the female partner holding her man's penis in an orgasm-inhibiting grip.

These mechanical sexual problems can usually be re-versed or treated one way or another, given the right motivation. But the main source of distress appears to be something which is not physical – loss of libido. Yet the very second we stop thinking of ourselves primarily as sexual beings, and stop worrying about performance, ejaculation or libido, all these problems disappear. With them, a whole enormous burden of worry, guilt and fear vanishes too. The importance a 'good' sex life has assumed in recent years can be judged by a recent court case where an infant-school teacher whose sex life had suffered as the result of an injury was awarded the sum of £26,198 damages. She was aged 53 at the time!

Though sex, or at least the expectation of it, may be detrimental to health in general by adding to the sum of stresses on the body, there are also of course some extremely specific ways in which sexual intercourse can harm health. One of these is cervical cancer. Once a very rare disease, suffered mainly by women over the age of 35, it is now becoming increasingly common in women of an ever-younger age. One of the main reasons for this is physical sex.

Dr Robert Yule, who has carried out a great deal of research into cervical cancer, has found that incidence of this disease is specifically related to age at first inter-course. The earlier a girl starts having sex, the more likelihood there is that the cells covering the cervix are damaged. These cells do not become fully mature until a woman is aged 19 or so, but most girls now have sex far younger than this.

Before the age of 19, the cervical cells are constantly changing and are extremely vulnerable to attack. It seems from what we know so far about cervical cancer that the main carcinogen – cancer-causing agent – here is the man's penis. The culprit may be a virus passed on at intercourse, or it may possibly be the sperm themselves. Nobody yet knows for sure, though findings currently suggest that it is more likely to be the sperm that act as carcinogens. These consist mainly of protein and may well be regarded by the body as foreign. The fact that the body does not always accept the sperm may result in pre-cancerous changes in the immature cells of the cervix. It is now known that those who lead celibate lives – for example, nuns – simply never succumb to cervical cancer, whereas prostitutes and other sexually promiscuous women are greatly at risk. In fact, the more times a woman has sex and the more frequently she changes partners the greater are her chances of contracting cervical cancer. This form of cancer can, we know, in some cases be treated and there is a great amount of pressure going on for screening to be available to all women who may be at risk. But nobody has ever suggested – or even dared to suggest – that sexual abstinence might be tried instead, despite the undisputed fact of the close link between sex and the onset of this life-threatening disease. Nowadays many people feel they just cannot give up sex, whatever the price may be. There is the feeling that life simply would not be worth living if sex had to be forgone, even when health and life are demonstrably endangered.

The other big health concern for women which is directly related to frequency of sex is cystitis. This uncomfortable, incurable and occasionally serious bladder complaint is one of the most common sex-related disorders, with about eight million attacks occurring each year in the UK alone. The condition used to be known as 'honeymoon cystitis', so commonly did it used to develop just after the marriage in the days when more brides were virgins on their wedding night. It tends to attack during honeymoons or other periods of intense sexual activity when the sexual organs are given little time to recover.

Cystitis is most often caused by a bacterium known as *Escherichia coli*, or *E. coli*, which lives in the bowel but which in women can all too easily be transferred to the urethra. About 50 per cent of female cystitis is started in this way. It seems that the bacteria are pushed into the vagina during intercourse, where they infect the area and can cause great pain.

Angela Kilmartin, the woman who first brought the hitherto unmentionable subject of cystitis into the open and who has written several best-selling books on it, once said at a conference: 'Your sex drive accounts for a vast amount of cystitis.' In the old days, there was probably less sexual intercourse, and there were correspondingly fewer attacks of cystitis. As with cervical cancer, abstinence from sex tends to cure the problem in no time at all. Yet it is never suggested as effective treatment, and instead, women liable to cystitis may be subjected to antibiotics – which actually lower resistance to infection – or even surgical procedures which by no means always work.

Cystitis, which is characterized by a frequent desire to urinate and an agonizing burning sensation when doing so, is another condition which is unknown amongst celibate women. In an important study referred to earlier, 2302 white working women were compared to 2882 white nuns in similar jobs, for frequency of bacteriuria, or urinary tract infections. It was found that the frequency of bacteriuria was very low indeed among nuns and also that the complaint occurred half as frequently in single as in married women. The researchers wrote in their report, published in the *New England Journal of Medicine* in 1968: 'The findings strongly suggest not only that celibacy has an important role in protection from bacteriuria, but also that girls destined to be nuns differ distinctly in susceptibility to urinary colonizations from girls and women in the general population.' Abstention from sexual contact of any kind is an important factor in freedom from bacterial infections of the urinary tract.

Apart from any transference of bacteria through intercourse, the condition can also result from bruising during sex. In fact, the more violent the sex, the more chance there is of bruising occurring. One reason why cystitis is so much on the increase – apart from the actual increase in sexual activity – is that the bacteria themselves are becoming ever more resistant to the antibiotics commonly used. In rare cases, cystitis can cause irreversible kidney damage, so it is not always the comparatively trivial and localized complaint that some people have regarded it as. Moreover it tends to recur and has no permanent cure.

During the 1960s, the decade of the so-called 'sexual revolution', sex was for the very first time effectively separated from fear of unwanted pregnancy by the invention of the contraceptive pill. The pill, which was blessed by a generation of women, gave hitherto unprecedented sexual freedom and was at first hailed as the true female liberator of all time. It meant, as we thought then, that we could be wonderfully free from any sexual hang-ups. If there was no possibility whatever of unwanted pregnancy occurring, there was also no need to fear sex any more. Instead of being frightened and wary, we women could now take the lead in sexual matters, assert ourselves, stop being timid and become sexually aggressive, if we so desired. We imagined that once the spectre of unwanted pregnancy was removed forever, there would be no limitations any more to our having complete sexual enjoyment and fulfilment. Now, of course, we know differently. The contraceptive pill, easily the most studied and widely researched drug in history, is now associated with many health problems, including subfertility, depression, allergies, thrombosis, breast cancer, mineral imbalances, migraine, strokes – to name just a few. Some women, those blessed with extra robust systems, do not seem to suffer from the pill, but it is the view of Dr Ellen Grant, author of *The Bitter Pill* and a leading researcher into the effect of oral contraceptives on health, that the synthetic hormones involved in the pill cause widespread havoc to body systems. The upsurge in cervical cancer is caused, she believes, jointly by the pill and the general increase in sexual activity, which itself has been made possible largely by the pill.

The pill is one of the few types of strong medication that are taken by people who are not ill. Instead of correcting something abnormal, it actually prevents the normal workings of the female reproductive system so that fertilization cannot take place. Its only function is to enable people to have sex without the risk of pregnancy. We are now learning, however, that there may actually be a huge price to pay, not only for the health of the present generation but also for those of the future. Some authorities believe that hyperactivity and allergies in children – two conditions which appear to be greatly on the increase – can also in part be related back to the pill.

In the 'sixties, we believed that sex was so important that it was worth searching for the perfect contraceptive. Many of those at the forefront of women's liberation at the time were urging young women to throw off the sexual repressions which had hampered the previous generation and take the initiative in sex. Germaine Greer, now a vociferous opponent of the pill, was an early advocate of uninhibited, untrammelled sex. Now she has changed her tune. Her recent book *Sex and Destiny* is largely devoted to describing the havoc that chemical birth control and the easy availability of women's bodies for sex have caused. Dr Greer has changed her tune because, like so many intelligent and aware women, she can no longer ignore the evidence that modern forms of contraception are very damaging to health, and also that by helping to foster the attitude that sex should always be available on demand they have ultimately lowered the esteem in which humans hold each other.

A propos of the pill, she writes:

We women who seized on the pill before it was ever released for routine use as a contraceptive fought to gain access to it, convinced that institutionalized sexual repression would keep it from general distribution for years. Those were the high-dose oestrogen pills, but when our heads ached, our ankles swelled, our breasts grew tender and we had bouts of morning sickness, we put it down to everything but the oral contraceptive. One day, after bursting into tears five times at work for no reason, I decided that the pill was the only possible cause. "Oh no," said my doctor, "there's no evidence for that sort of effect." There is now.

Nor is oral contraception the only kind which may affect health adversely. The IUD, or intra-uterine device, preferred by some women as it does not interfere with the body's hormone balance in a general way, can nevertheless create many health problems of its own. Many women find that insertion is agonizingly painful and that it causes, at the very least, heavy periods which may at times amount to severe haemorrhaging. As we know, the IUD is not, strictly speaking, a contraceptive at all, but a method of preventing a possibly fertilized egg from attaching itself to the uterus and growing into a baby. Many IUDs are made of copper, and may cause increased levels of this mineral – which is toxic in large amounts – to circulate in the body. As the IUD is a foreign body, it is not actually welcomed or wanted by the uterus, which tries to expel it. It also seems that the IUD may work to change the cell structure within the womb. Nobody knows for sure exactly what damage the IUD may bring about or how it may affect surrounding cells, but Germaine Greer says in her book that dissected wombs of deceased IUD-users show many disturbing cell and tissue changes and erosions.

Many women find that they cannot physically tolerate the presence of an IUD and that the pain resulting from its insertion never subsides. The increased blood loss could be serious for some women, and there is certainly an increased risk of an ectopic pregnancy, in which the baby gets stuck in the Fallopian tubes instead of growing properly in the uterus. Ectopic pregnancies cause death unless surgery is carried out immediately on diagnosis. Pelvic inflammatory disease (PID) is another unwelcome and well-known side effect of the IUD.

Professors Martin Vessey and Richard Doll, who have carried out much research into the health hazards of the pill, have also reported that IUDs can cause 'uterine perforation and pelvic inflammatory disease. In addition, unplanned pregnancies occuring in women using an intra-uterine device are much more likely to be ectopic or end in spontaneous abortion than usual, and there is some evidence that such abortions are particularly likely to be septic, occasionally with fatal results for the mother.' (This report was published in *Proceedings of the Royal Society*, 1976.)

Depo-Provera, the injectable hormonal contraceptive which, like the pill, works by suppressing ovulation, also alters the lining of the womb so that it rejects any fertilized egg. At the very least, this contraceptive causes irregular bleeding and its main problem seems to be that the injection affects all women differently. Some will have no bleeding at all for the three months the injection lasts, while others bleed almost continuously; many women undergo considerable weight changes while taking DP and blood-clotting mechanisms may be affected as well. A World Health Organization paper reported a definite increase in cervical cancer rates after five years of DP use.

The three main modern contraceptives for women have all been designed in the belief that an unwanted pregnancy was the only real adverse effect of sexual intercourse. Now we know that these artificial chemical compounds and metal devices set up many adverse reactions which may have long-term consequences. It appears that the basic biochemistry of the body does not welcome a constant supply of synthetic hormones which alter the balance set up by nature, nor does the system like to have a copper wire in the womb.

Most of the modern contraceptives have been designed to be used by women, to enable them to shake off the curse of centuries and to allow them to have sex without adding to the world's population. It is doubtful, however, that women's bodies were designed to cope with the continuous onslaught of very frequent sex not primarily intended for procreation. The alarming rise in cases of cervical cancer and cystitis alone should warn us. In most cases, however, it has not. Treatments for these conditions never include recommendations to abstain from sex. Indeed, today's medications for these disorders are specifically designed so that it is possible to go on having sex.

Men do not escape the health consequences of unlimited sex. Though their bodies may not suffer in quite the same direct way, there is undoubtedly a price to be paid in terms of physical health. Herpes, AIDS and other sexually-transmitted diseases such as non-specific urethritis – which affects mainly men – are all greatly on the increase.

Even vasectomy, that 'simple little operation', as it has been called, is not without possible adverse health consequences. The only reason a man has a vasectomy is to enable him to go on having sex without fear of reproduction. For many men, this would seem to be an unmitigated blessing, especially if they have already reproduced and do not want more children. But there have been some recent reports that vasectomy – after which sperm can no longer escape from the penis – can cause premature ageing, and can be a factor in certain conditions such as atherosclerosis. According to one authority, vasectomy can produce changes in the immune system of about half the men who have the operation. We now know that complex biological reactions occur after vasectomy, and that the immune system can attack the sperm, which are still produced but which no longer have an outlet. As one doctor said: 'The body does not like being attacked, and can pay you back in a roundabout fashion'. It appears that vasectomy may also result in veins becoming clogged up in some men.

A relatively new discovery is that frequent sex may cause a man to become deficient in zinc, now recognized as one of the most essential trace minerals. Zinc is necessary for a multitude of biochemical functions, and whenever deficiency occurs, illness, depressive conditions and – in men – infertility may result. The recommended daily intake of zinc is 15 milligrams per day for an adult. In most Western countries, however, far less than this is taken in, and an average amount for most men would be 10 mg. Zinc levels are further depleted by stress, junk foods, alcohol and cigarettes. Zinc is especially needed for the formation of active sperm and it is estimated that one seminal emission costs a man one milligram of zinc. This may be a substantial proportion of what he is taking in his daily diet. The other factor is that zinc is now known to affect brain function, and what is lost from the penis is also lost from the brain, by an equal amount. So, in a roundabout way, frequent sex could serve to make a man less intelligent. Certainly those who need to conserve their physical or mental strength before a major event in their lives – such as a sporting challenge – know from ancient wisdom that they should abstain from sex beforehand, and athletes are still advised not to have sex for up to two weeks before a big race or match.

Men who are unable to have a proper sexual relationship are often advised to masturbate. Modern medical books pour scorn on the old idea – now dismissed as an old wives' tale – that masturbation can make you go blind. But our new knowledge of how zinc works in the body tells us that this idea is, actually, *not* nonsense. Apart from its function in growth, maturity and efficiency of the sexual organs, large amounts of zinc are needed for sight. Indeed, photophobia, or ultra-sensitivity to light, is a well-known side effect of zinc deficiency. Thus, frequent sex and frequent masturbation – both of which deplete zinc levels – *can* adversely affect a man's eyesight, as well as his general health and intellectual capacity. Zinc is also needed for proper functioning of the immune system, so zinc lost through sex could also decrease resistance to all kinds of common infections. Zinc is less intimately needed for female sex organs, and as women have no ejaculate (unless you believe the authors of *The G-spot*) no valuable body fluid escapes from them during sexual activity.

Now we come to the specifically sexually transmitted diseases. Gonorrhea and syphilis have for centuries been a worry for those who indulge in casual sex. There is a frightening account of how easily it can be caught in James Boswell's *London Journal*, written in 1762–3. These 'big-time' STDs can now be completely cured and are therefore less of a bogey than they were in former times, but others have come in to take their place. The commonest STD for men is non-specific urethritis, usually termed NSU, in which there is an unpleasant discharge from the urethra and pain in the genital area.

Genital herpes, which first became a problem in the early 'eighties, is caused by the cold-sore virus which produces painful, burning blisters in the genital area. Both men and women can contract herpes, which at the moment is untreatable and incurable. About one-third of sufferers experience a tingling pain down the legs, and also back pain and fever. Once the blisters appear, they can recur several times a year.

Hepatitis-B, a virus disease that can be extremely serious, may also be transmitted through sexual intercourse. This liver complaint is complicated by the fact that there is no possible way of detecting carriers.

But all these STDs, though problematic enough for

sufferers, have paled into insignificance with the advent of AIDS. AIDS, or acquired immune deficiency syndrome, is the horrific sexual scourge of the 'eighties, and has already become a world-wide epidemic. The condition, first diagnosed in promiscuous homosexuals in America, is currently untreatable. So far, nobody has ever recovered from the clinical form of the disease.

Briefly, AIDS is caused by a virus, HTLV-111 (human T-cell lymphotropic virus type 3), which destroys immune function once it gets into the bloodstream. Not everybody who is diagnosed antibody-positive and therefore carries the virus will succumb to the clinical form of the condition, but all those who have frequent sexual contact with a large variety of partners may be considered to be at risk. AIDS is transmitted only by transference of body fluids, either through sex or from blood transfusions. There is no other way of contracting the disease, which can cause a form of cancer, Kaposi's sarcoma, which attacks the skin. Sufferers also fall prey to other 'opportunistic' infections.

The main point about AIDS is that almost all of those who succumb to the clinical form of the disease are living a physically chaotic life. Frequent promiscuous sex seems almost always to go with a generally unhealthy lifestyle – smoking, drinking, not eating properly. Those who are supremely fit and well and who are not having frequent sex would probably not go down with AIDS, though they may be carriers of the virus. It appears that the pursuit of sex *in itself* weakens the body's defences against ill health. So far, all AIDS victims have been suffering from generally very poor health, as well as from extreme stress, even though many victims have been young men without any other apparent physical diseases.

Many books have now been written about AIDS, and the search is now on for a vaccine that will be effective against the virus. Some people have predicted that AIDS will, if nothing else, bring about the end of the sexual revolution as we have known it. The Indian guru Bhagwan Shree Rajneesh (for what his views may be worth) has predicted that AIDS will eventually kill two-thirds of humanity. It has been lamented that there is no cure for AIDS – but there is: abstention from sex. However, nobody likes to admit this. Instead we are given advice on how to have 'safe sex'.

In their book *AIDS: the Deadly Epidemic* Graham Hancock and Enver Carim write:

> Becoming celibate does seem rather drastic, but with death from AIDS almost a daily occurrence in San Francisco, and funerals in that beautiful city a regular part of popular culture, the value of life is being re-emphasized for many young people who are discovering that certain forms of behaviour just aren't worth the price that might have to be paid for them.

The authors go on to say that clear evidence has emerged in West Germany that the epidemic's driving force was promiscuity rather than actual sexual orientation. For a while, it was assumed that AIDS was a homosexual's disease, as only those with homosexual inclinations seemed to contract it, at least in the West. But now we know that the more sex partners a person has – of whatever gender – the higher are his or her chances of contracting the virus. Doctors now diagnosing AIDS say that a promiscuous way of life, often with several different partners a week, practised for years on end (a not uncommon lifestyle for many homosexuals), leads to a degree of vulnerability to the infection that is 'way above average'. The patients who went down with AIDS when it was first diagnosed had all contracted gonorrhea several times and were, almost without exception, infected with the herpes virus as well. A full 96 per cent showed hepatitis-B in their history and 90 per cent showed syphilis as well.

But even faced with this world epidemic for which there is currently no medical cure, people are reluctant to lead a life of celibacy. There have been calls for 'safer sex', and both condoms and rubber gloves are now often used during sex owing to the fear of AIDS being transmitted. Yet, just by stopping sex, the disease could be completely eradicated. It is extremely difficult to lead a generally healthy lifestyle while indulging in promiscuous sex. At the very least, as we have seen, frequent sex leads to increased arousal which in turn leads to stress. In addition, a considerable expenditure of energy is involved in actually finding all the different partners. Though many male homosexuals do not want an emotional relationship with their sexual partners, they cannot always avoid this, and they go through the whole gamut of attraction, rejection, rage, fear, anger, jealousy and lust, which all place added stresses on the system.

Hancock and Enver write:

The changing of sex partners, the random sleeping around . . . was of course, a way of life that "liberated" heterosexual men and women preferred until three or four years into the epidemic. It was taken to be a sign of sophistication, as was sniffing coke and downing speed.

It seems abundantly clear that from the point of view of health celibacy is a far better bet than promiscuous sexual activity. The fact that frequent sex can cause or exacerbate so many diseases and illnesses must raise the question as to how far sex can be considered a 'natural' activity. Obviously it cannot be natural to be ill and under great stress all the time. Nor does the body enjoy being in a state of continuous arousal, experiencing wild hormonal fluctuations or being dosed up with artificial chemicals. At the very least, to be sexually active means that the body is rarely in a calm, peaceful state. And it is the calm state, we now know, that is most conducive to long-term physical health.

CHAPTER 4

Celibacy and young people

A generation ago, there were very few sex-education books written specifically for young people apart from those of the 'Where did I come from?' variety. In consequence, those of us who grew up in the 'fifties and 'sixties had to rely on such information as we could glean from our more enlightened friends, from women's magazines – far and away the best and most accurate source of information – and from biology lessons at school. It seemed to us then that there was a conspiracy to keep any proper knowledge away from us, in case we found out and then went and did it.

All that has certainly changed dramatically, and now, in the 'eighties, there is a positive avalanche of sex books for teenagers, which seem to pour almost daily off the presses. The books are being written mainly by people who were adolescent in the 'sixties, in the well-meant belief that the present generation should not be allowed to grow up as woefully ignorant as we did. As well as sex manuals for teenagers, which are often extremely sexually explicit, there are also countless programmes on the subject on television.

The result is that there can now be hardly a teenager in the land who does not know exactly what fellatio and cunnilingus are, for example, or precisely where the erogenous zones are, when ovulation occurs, and just what happens to sex organs before, during and after intercourse. Contraception, which in my far-off teenage-hood was a subject not talked about, even in hushed tones, is now on many O- and A-level syllabuses. In the same way that we remained in ignorance, or were deliberately kept in ignorance, so today's teenagers are bombarded with sex advice from every quarter, and from every section of the media.

Special clinics to advise young people on sexual matters

have been established for some time now and the Family Planning Association is constantly issuing explanatory leaflets aimed at this age-group. There are even sex books written for young children which go so far as to explain what an orgasm feels like: 'a great big sneeze' was how this sensation was described in one such book.

Almost all the former taboos surrounding sex have now broken down and I understand that young people today are quite relaxed and unembarrassed about discussing matters that had us blushing to the roots of our hair and beyond. Boys and girls talk quite happily together, and quite openly, about menstruation, condoms, erections and anal sex whereas not long ago they would never be mentioned in mixed company.

Not only do the present-day teenage sex manuals explain everything anybody could want to know about sex and more, they also show in anatomically detailed illustrations exactly how one has sex. Many of these manuals verge distinctly on the pornographic, and I suspect a lot of them are bought by dirty old men rather than the 16- to 18-year-olds they are theoretically aimed at, though they are, in the main, marketed through educational channels. Some sex books for adolescents show very young naked couples in bed together, or fondling each other in intimate fashion.

The messages that run through most of the sex books for the teenage market is that sex is o.k. – provided, of course, that the participants have already built up a loving, caring relationship. In surveys on sex conducted by teenage magazines, most respondents say they would certainly have to be in love before thinking about sex. But as Germaine Greer pointed out in an article in the *Mail on Sunday* in February, 1985: 'Can't anybody remember how easy it was to be in love when she was a teenager?'

I, as a teenager, was at different times 'desperately' in love with Dirk Bogarde, my history master, the head boy, the leader of a youth club I attended, Kenneth Allsop (a TV personality of the 'fifties and 'sixties), the poet Rupert Brooke and other people whom I scarcely knew or did not even know at all. I suspect teenagers of today are hardly any different. Falling in love is part of the process of growing up, and we are all wildly in love for much of our adolescence. Luckily, we grow out of it – or should do.

The plethora of information, of soft-porn pictures and all-too-explicit advice from those who set themselves up as 'experts' – and the qualification for becoming an expert nowadays is usually a medical degree – has already resulted in a reaction of some kind. Concerned that today's youth were being fed too many images about the rightness of sex, the so-called Responsible Society in 1985 issued a video, coyly entitled *Let's Talk About Love*, to try to stem the current idea that sex between consenting teenagers is normal and should be encouraged. The Responsible Society is advocating a return to traditional values and has become the stern voice of a moralistic outlook. The video tells the story of two girls, June and Linda, who are of the same age but very different in outlook. June has sex with a variety of partners at a very early age and, as a result, has to have an abortion; she ends up in a dead-end job as a waitress.

By contrast, Linda decides to remain a virgin and, as a direct consequence, passes all her exams, goes to college and ends her fairytale existence by marrying in white in a country church, enviously watched by June. The message is all too clear: the wages of early, promiscuous sin are waitressing, abortions and no white wedding.

In recommending today's young people to consider celibacy as a positive option, I must emphasize that I am *not* on the side of the Responsible Society, nor do I endorse at all the views expressed on the video. Linda, the prissy, self-satisfied virgin, is to me a far less sympathetic character than June, who is at least real. But the true perniciousness of the video is that it harks back to the old idea that, for a girl, her virginity is her market value, and that if she hangs on to it she will eventually marry Mr Right in a flurry of white tulle and stephanotis, 'given away' by her father. The very worst aspect of this video is that it represents a church wedding and marriage as the apogee of female achievement. Many girls would, I am sure, rather live an independent life as a waitress than be a blushing bride who believes in chastity before marriage and fidelity afterwards, condemned to a lifetime of being nothing more than 'Mrs Him'.

My reason for encouraging a positive view of celibacy

has nothing whatever to do with premarital chastity. Sexual intercourse is sexual intercourse: it is the same act whether or not the participants have walked up the aisle and said 'I do' first. But I am against sex at too early an age for either boys or girls, because I believe that a non-sexual period between childhood and adulthood helps both boys and girls to grow up to be independent, self-reliant and self-confident. Apart from the health dangers discussed in the previous chapter, there is the very considerable risk that young people will grow up expecting others to take care of them, make them happy and 'complete' them, if they start having sex too soon.

This chapter is not addressed to those girls – or young men – who believe in keeping themselves for Mr or Miss Right. It is addressed to the youth of both sexes who want to know how to be truly themselves, to find out who they are, who want to be healthy, strong and self-reliant, sure in the knowledge that they can, if they so wish, walk through life without a crutch and the dependence of a sexual involvement with another human being. Many of today's supposedly grown-up people have remained adolescents at heart – timid, fearful, dependent people who have never learned how to look after themselves. For many people, physical sex is the adult equivalent of hugging a teddy bear, or a security blanket. The difference is that with sex, another person's emotions, life and well-being inevitably become involved.

To me, there is no real difference in sex before or after marriage. As it is the same act, it brings identical emotions in its wake, and the question of whether or not one has made a 'commitment' to another person is largely irrelevant.

Young unmarried people of today may, if they choose, have a sexual relationship, as there is no longer a cultural taboo against it. But what is not always realized is that one can also choose not to, and that the latter choice has many benefits which can override the search for constant, blissful sex.

Though I do not like most of the sex manuals on sale today, regarding them as pornographic, prurient and patronizing, neither am I advocating a return to the dark days of ignorance, confusion and bewilderment that my own generation lived through. What I most object to in the manuals is the message that love and sex are inextricably intertwined, and that if you love a person you will naturally want to have sexual intercourse with them. In fact, the opposite could be argued: if you truly love a person, you will *not* want to have sex with them, as the relationship will then be one of true minds rather than of bodies.

The present-day sex books also put across the completely erroneous fantasy that sex with the one you 'love' will be akin to a religious experience – blissful, ecstatic and transcendental. Few people find this in real life, at least after the first few sessions when the relationship is new. At these times, when one is first attracted to another person, just touching hands can be an electric experience. For those very newly in love, just to be in the same room as the loved one can be enough to bring about transports of delight.

Sex is not 'better' or 'worse' necessarily because you are, or want for the time being to believe you are, in love with the other person. It is just a physical act, neutral in itself, and we endow it with whatever meaning we choose at that particular time. We humans have, over the centuries, woven complicated fantasies into the sexual act, and glorified it with mystical significance. This being so, we can be extremely disappointed when it does not live up to expectations, and blame the other person involved for not being attractive enough, or a sufficient turn-on. Very many boys are disappointed with their girlfriends when they have sex together and may accuse the girl of being frigid, unsensuous or non-reactive if she has been completely passive throughout. Having sex together is usually the start of the lovers hurting each other's feelings and very often marks the downturn of the friendship.

At this point, there may be howls of rage from those who ask me to consider the positive aspects of sex for young people. Does it not bring people closer together? they may ask; does it not make people warmer and more human, and does it not release pent-up longings and frustrations? Does it not in fact, make people feel alive, wanted, earthy, in touch with their senses and emotions? My detractors could also point to the wealth of literature, from ancient times to our own, which has glorified the sexual act and enshrined it in memorable verse. If sex were as wrong as I make out, why do so many people experience that spiritual fusing through sex, and feel that for the time being they are truly one flesh, and that they will not be divided?

My answer to these objections is that yes, sex may possibly appear to do wonderful things for people. It can be the most powerful placebo known and participants can truly, honestly imagine that they are being elevated and made better people for the experience. But at the same time one must always remember that sex necessarily involves another person, whose feelings may be very much less intense than one's own. One of the most famous pleas for sexual intercourse in the English language, Andrew Marvell's 'To His Coy Mistress', is a lover's attempt to persuade his extremely reluctant mistress to yield up her virginity to him. The lover has to resort to threats, insults and moral blackmail to persuade the lady to give in to him. 'Had we but world enough and time,' he begins, 'This coyness, lady, were no crime,' then goes on to tell her what will happen if she continues to refuse him: 'then [after death] worms shall try/That long-preserv'd virginity.'

Though this is a very well-known poem, it is hardly famous for having the best interests of the woman at heart. The lover is trying to force her into sex. If she agrees, the experience may be wonderful for him, but will it be so marvellous for her?

If we look through literature at the world's greatest love stories, we find that, in almost every case, there were tragic endings. One thinks of Romeo and Juliet, Heloise and Abelard, Troilus and Cressida, Paris and Helen, Lancelot and Guinevere. In most cases, sex was their downfall rather than their upliftment. Whatever bliss was attained in each other's arms, it was extremely short-lived, and the lovers suffered greatly, mainly as a result of their attachment for one another.

We can bestow on the physical act of sex whatever emotions we choose, but we should recognize that a physical union of bodies can never bring about, or contibute to, lasting personal happiness.

The mistake we have made today – and with desperate results for today's young people – is that we have elevated sex beyond all sense and reason, and imbued it with a deep spiritual meaning which it should not have. Adolescents who, like all of us, naturally long for transcendental bliss and ecstatic, transporting experiences, can mistakenly believe they will gain these by having sex at a very young age, long before any kind of emotional maturity is reached and often, these days, before physical maturity is reached. Sex, for very young people, can be a slightly more sophisticated version of the thrill experienced not many years earlier at funfairs, or when climbing trees. The difference, always, is that childish pleasures could be enjoyed alone whereas with sex, apart from the *ersatz* thrill of masturbation, this is impossible. As sex always involves somebody else, it often involves threats, inducements, cajoling, wheedling, coyness – any number of negative and undignified persuasion techniques.

A recent survey in *True Romances* magazine revealed that the average age of first intercourse in the UK was 16½. This is far too young, for at this age there has been no chance for the phase of adolescence to pass and be superseded by true maturity. A girl who has sex so very young risks becoming fixed forever in the adolescent phase, expecting always that wiles, sexy ways and seductive behaviour will achieve what she wants in life. She will be in danger of growing up as somebody who always has to rely on others and is ill-equipped to face life on her own.

Physical sex is rarely a nightmare for boys – unless they become tortured by its absence in their lives – but it can be either enjoyable, neutral or horrific for girls, depending on how, where and with whom the act is carried out. We are learning now that fear of an unwanted pregnancy is by no means the only, or even perhaps the major, anxiety that young women associate with sex.

If a father, stepfather or uncle forces a child to have sex – which is a by no means uncommon occurrence, as we now know – the act and all memories of it will be terrifying. If a young girl, or indeed any woman of any age, is raped by a stranger, this too is regarded as horrific. If a boy she does not find particularly attractive pressurizes a girl into sex and she eventually agrees, to keep the peace, she may find the whole experience either completely devoid of sensation or mildly or extremely distasteful. For women, there is simply no pleasure in the sex act for itself: the whole thing depends on their relationship to the other person at the time of intercourse.

If the girl in question is desperately in love with the man she considers the most handsome, the most attractive, the most desirable in the world, then sex with him can be a transporting experience, even if the man is actually, in the physical sense, an indifferent lover. Most women find that enjoyment or otherwise of sex depends almost totally on the partner, and their current relationship to this person. The handsome, desirable lover may turn, over the years, into a boring, staid husband, at which time sex with him will not be so exciting. Indeed, it will have become a tedious chore.

Even when one does love, or is at least fond of, the other person, sex never remains exciting for very long. In his book *Love's Mysteries*, psychologist Glenn Wilson reported that the only time women experience ardour and sexual excitement equal to that of a man is at the very start of a new relationship. After nine to eighteen months, she becomes less interested in sex, however much she may have wanted it at first.

There is some evidence that boys, in the main, do not have the same attitude as girls to sex, and that the old 'double standard' still applies, at least to some extent. As males cannot be raped – except perhaps in a homosexual manner – or become pregnant, they have far less to fear from the sex act. As a result, they almost always enjoy intercourse. Young males of today, from about the age of 16 onwards, seem to be desperate for sex and spend much of their time, thought and energy trying to persuade girls of their acquaintance to 'sleep' with them. The common desire among male adolescents seems to be for girls to be more ready, willing and eager for sex without the boys having to engage in what they view as emotional hassles or to establish an exclusive, loving relationship with the girl first.

We now have the understanding that teenagers are extremely sexual creatures whose coursing hormones make them want to have intercourse at a very young age. Older people who want to appear liberal-minded take the attitude that one should not deny adolescents the natural expression of their sexuality. My own argument is rather different. I feel that we have foisted sexuality on to our youth and made them think about sex when they could be thinking about other things. I feel that we adults are now doing all we possibly can to encourage our young people to have sexual relationships, and with as great a variety of partners as possible. As with everything else, there is a mixture of motives in all this. Those who are now in their thirties and forties – the ones who were young when the present sexual revolution was in its infancy – are anxious for their own children to have the sexual freedom they themselves were denied. At the same time, there is a degree of prurience about it all, typified by the debased currency of the ubiquitous 'glamour' shot and the many top-selling pornographic videos that show extremely young people, hardly more than children, engaging in sexual acts.

It is true, of course, that sex hormones are circulating at high levels in adolescence. This happens partly because nature is preparing children to be reproductive adults; however, the more the individual thinks about sex, the more this in itself encourages the appropriate hormones to be manufactured. Recent research has established that there are complicated interactions going on all the time between the mind and body, and that the mind can exert a powerful influence on bodily mechanisms.

It is also true that adolescents have complicated yearnings, longings and fantasies. But these would not necessarily be associated with physical sex, or with feeling frustrated and deprived, unless these messages are constantly being received from society. Sex books say that it is bad for people to become sexually aroused and then not to be able to satisfy the urge, and so we believe this to be true. Very many young people of today have come to feel that, unless they have a boyfriend or girlfriend with whom they are having sex, they are not really existing, that their youth is passing in a limbo of nothingness.

This idea is all, in fact, very new. In Victorian and Regency times – at least if the historical romances are to be believed – most educated, upper-class men did not even consider marriage until they were about 33 years of age. As unmarried women were not available for sex unless they were professional prostitutes, most men had to wait an awfully long time to give expression to their sexuality. We do not receive the impression however, that the sardonic Mr Darcy in Jane Austen's *Pride and Prejudice*, or Mr Knightley in *Emma*, pass their adult lives before marriage in an agony of sexual frustration. Nor do the heroines appear to be conscious that they are sexually deprived. Any frustrations, moments of depression or other malaise are put down to other causes, such as the weather or a bad cold.

Until the twentieth century, university students, too, were expected, even required, to be celibate. Until the nineteenth century, academics at Oxford and Cambridge, whatever their age, could not marry, and so had to choose between marriage and the academic life. Few of these men, however mature they may have been, would have had sexual outlets, and certainly for the students there would have been practically no opportunity at all for sexual liaisons.

When women's colleges were established, towards the end of the nineteenth century, there were very strict rules about fraternizing with male undergraduates. Girton College, for example, one of the pioneer women's colleges at Cambridge (now mixed), was established in a village three miles outside Cambridge for the sole purpose of separating the men from the women students.

One wonders whether all these students were perpetually sexually frustrated for the whole three years of their academic career? I doubt it very much indeed. Few probably even thought about sex, at least to any great extent. That was something that could easily be left until later, until the years of study were over.

During the 'sixties, it became fashionable to laugh at these puritanical, repressive rules; gradually restrictions were lifted and today most universities and colleges of further education are hotbeds of unrestricted, untrammelled sexual activity. A study conducted at Edinburgh University in 1985 discovered that the vast majority of students were having regular sex, on average every three or four weeks. Those who did not were distinctly in the minority.

We have to ask: what do people imagine is the benefit from all this increased sexual freedom among young people? Are students of today happier, healthier, better adjusted, more able to form lasting relationships, than students of earlier generations? Even the most vociferous of champions for sexual freedom would have to answer no, they are not. The suicide and attempted-suicide rates among young people are on the increase, and marriages are breaking up faster than ever before. It used to be the case that one in three marriages ended in divorce, but now the figure is getting nearer to one in two. The younger the age at which the marriage takes place, the more likely divorce is to happen.

At the same time as attempted suicides are increasing and marriages breaking up, the levels of educational attainment among the young are falling. It has been fashionable to blame falling standards of education on comprehensive schools, but another reason could be that many of today's young people are preoccupied with sex almost to the exclusion of anything else.

I now believe – and this is the complete opposite of what I believed twenty years ago – that sexual activity at too early an age contributes directly to stifled intelligence and educational achievement. Those who are concerned with having sex at a very young age are liable to concentrate less on their studies and examination results. After all, we have only a certain amount of energy, and the more that we dissipate in physical activities, the less will be available for mental pursuits. As I said earlier, sexual activity at a very young age also contributes to a lack of independence, and this too is associated with intelligence levels. The more intelligent a person is, the more independent-minded he or she can become. And intelligence is not a static, finite entity. It can be enlarged and increased, so long as it is nurtured in the right way.

Instead of being allowed to grow up properly, today's young people are becoming increasingly dependent on one another, on establishing relationships with the opposite sex and finding true love in one another's arms.They are learning to rely on other people to make them happy, rather than coming to the understanding that happiness is only ever possible once one has learned *not* to rely on others. To rely on other people means that one is going to be almost perpetually disappointed, as others will never come up to expectations. Indeed, why should they? In order to achieve true maturity, young people have to learn that other people do not have the power to confer happiness. While they are sexually dependent, they will never be able to learn this vital lesson.

Celibacy for young people used to be the norm but is now seen as distinctly unattractive and undesirable. Celibacy is seen in terms of coldness, lack of giving, selfishness, overvaluing virginity. Yet I believe that it is the only way of becoming fully adult, fully independent and fully mature. But, it must be emphasized, celibacy has value only when it has been freely chosen. A youth who remains celibate because he feels too shy, too unattractive, too short or too tall to find a girlfriend will never benefit from being celibate, because all the time he will be worrying about sex and wondering when, if ever, he is going to achieve success as a lover. Similarly, girls who are celibate but not from choice will tend to spend many miserable hours worrying about why they cannot seem to find a boyfriend, or why the handsome man of their dreams never materializes to sweep them off their feet.

Sex between young people always causes more problems than it solves, and, in the end, increases the sum of misery in their lives. On one level, there is the constant fear of pregnancy, unless the girl is taking the contraceptive pill. But though the pill successfully stops any possibility of pregnancy, evidence which can no longer be ignored concerning the multifarious health risks reveals that danger is being courted in another way. For males, energetic sexual activity can, as we have seen, lead to losses of valuable trace minerals from the brain and other parts of the body.

Perhaps even more damaging than the health risks in the long term are the emotional and mental consequences of believing that sex will be life-enhancing and happy. Boys may constantly long for sex and feel horribly deprived if they are not getting any, but in fact their real or imagined performance in this regard is a perpetual source of anxiety to them. Most boys worry about whether their sexual equipment is of the right size and shape, whether they will be able to maintain an erection, or whether, when they finally get to go to bed with a girl, it will all be over in half a minute or less, causing the girl to laugh at and deride them for their poor ability. Boys who are preoccupied with sex also spend much time worrying about whether they are attractive enough, or have the right sort of personality, to command a steady supply of girlfriends. Furthermore, the girls' capriciousness and contrariness (as they see it) worry and confuse them even more. Girls, annoyingly, are not content merely with physical sex, but often insist on having a proper relationship. The boy may not want this – only to perform the act of sex. Often, however, embarking on a 'steady' relationship is the only way a girl will allow him to have sexual intercourse with her. 'Why can't a girl be more like a boy?' the average male adolescent asks himself as he finds himself having to say 'Yes, I do love you' before the girl will even allow him to take off her cardigan. Boys soon learn that girls can, and do, bargain for sex. They say, 'I'll sleep with you if . . .' and then go on to make all kinds of conditions, which the boy finds distinctly disconcerting. Why can't girls just accept sex as a physical act, something rather like a game of football, or going to the cinema? But the boy soon discovers that they can't or won't. Very many boys, especially those who are too immature for a proper relationship, would like girls to behave like inflatable dolls – always eager, always ready, always smiling, and never making a nuisance of themselves. Alternatively, they dream of finding a sophisticated, slightly older woman who will agree to sex all the time without making any demands whatever on her young lover. Few, needless to say, ever find this paragon.

Any sexual relationship will moreover bring into being feelings of jealousy and possession. Any girl who has agreed to sexual intercourse will feel highly affronted and 'used' if her boy establishes another relationship of a sexual nature at the same time. The boy may argue that he can like two girls at once, but most girls feel they want to have an exclusive love affair, especially if sex is involved. A time-honoured euphemism for sexual intercourse is 'possession'; lovers do truly feel that they possess each other and can therefore make claims on each other. They can become consumed with rage when 'their' lover embarks on another partnership. Love can then in an instant turn to hate. Jealousy can also drive out feelings of love, and make the lover actually want to kill the person who has dared to regard someone else in a sexual way. Most people find that sex, rather than strengthening bonds, actually loosens them and drives people apart. One can remain friends with members of the opposite sex with whom one has not had a sexual relationship, but it becomes difficult to do this once sex enters the picture, especially when one is young. When an affair ends, the lovers often never speak to each other again for the rest of their lives. The hurt can remain for many, many years, and never finally die away.

For girls, especially, it may be that sex adds yet one more worry to an already worry-filled life. It was observed earlier that more young people of both sexes were attempting suicide. An astonishing survey conducted by the teenage magazine *Look Now* and published in April, 1986, revealed that one in ten girls between the ages of 15 and 17 attempt suicide, and more than one-third of girls in that age-group at some time consider ending their lives. More than half the girls questioned said they were afraid to go out after dark, and nearly one in five had been sexually assaulted or even raped.

The survey, mounted to discover just how much young girls are suffering from stress, found that the greatest single cause of misery was over love and sexual relationships. Over 37 per cent of the 2000 respondents said that they had experienced the break-up of a close relationship over the past year, and more than one in five admitted to having sexual problems. About 50 per cent said they worried constantly about pregnancy and contraception. The level of stress associated with boyfriends was leading, according to the survey, to headaches, dizziness, insomnia and nausea.

If the sexual revolution had delivered what it promised, today's girls would be gloriously happy, revelling in their sexual feelings and the fact that they are at last able to express them without inhibition and without worry. The promise was that, once the shackles of Victorian repression were finally shed, everybody would be able to make love in a glorious, carefree way, as one (possibly erroneously) imagines South Sea islanders are doing all the time.

The fact is that the present generation of teenagers is not carefree and uninhibited. The greater freedom over sexual matters has brought yet more burdens, not allowed those already with us to be shed.

There are several reasons for this. One is that, as sex is around us all the time, more and more youngsters, especially boys, become convinced they are entitled to have sex and feel something is wrong if it does not take place. One result of this belief is that there are ever more gang rapes by very young boys. These are on the increase all the time, as is sexual abuse of pre-adolescent children. Nobody can argue with this. It is a fact that the incidence of rape is increasing each year. A girl of 15 ought to be able to go out alone after dark in perfect safety. Yet the attitude of many people in some parts of the UK now and also, as I understand it, in much of America, is that if a teenage girl is out walking alone after dark and is raped, she has in some way asked for it.

Another reason for greater unhappiness over sexual matters is that boys and girls who do not have exclusive partners often become very miserable and withdrawn. There appears to be pressure to pair off at an ever-earlier age; children of 13 years old and less now boast of their 'boyfriends' and 'girlfriends'. The fear of being alone and without a partner is one reason why so many youngsters are making suicide attempts and taking drug overdoses.

A third reason why the present emphasis on sexual fulfilment at an early age is upsetting, especially for girls, is that it leads to poor performance in school and academic work. The art teacher Gordon Gillick, husband of Victoria (the famous campaigner against contraceptives for under-age girls), said in an interview recently: 'Once a girl has had sex, she loses interest in academic matters. She just becomes usable. And the sad thing is that she hasn't had a chance to find herself and probably never will.'

Much educational research in recent years has shown

that girls are always ahead of boys academically until puberty, when they start to slacken off. The main reason for this is not that girls suddenly lose their intelligence at the same time as they acquire secondary sexual character- istics, but that the focus of their attention shifts away from their studies and towards the boys in the class. By the time they reach the age of 13 or 14 they are competing, not for top place, but for the boys' attention. Instead of doing their homework, they will spend hours dressing up and making up, simply to attract boys. They succeed in ensnaring a boy, get engaged and get married – then spend the rest of their lives miserably wondering what went wrong, and asking themselves whether this really is all there is to life. As Gordon Gillick so rightly pointed out, they have become 'usable' long before they ever gave themselves a chance to grow up or to learn how to become autonomous human beings. It is difficult to concentrate on academic work, which in its early stages can be both boring and unrewarding, if half your mind is occupied with boyfriend worries, or fears about becoming pregnant. Yet it is the academic and other personal achievements which last and which bring about worth- while rewards. Anyone at all can have sex – that does not take any intelligence, any personal merit – but effort is needed to attain personal success. The more sex a person has, the more the individual qualities tend to become lost. One girl constantly having sex is very much like another girl who is always having sex.

Am I saying then, that all teenagers should shun sex and wait until they are in their mid to late twenties – as they apparently do in communist China? If they want to realize themselves and their true potential then yes, there is a case to be made for delaying sexual involvement until true maturity is reached.

Before embarking on a sexual relationship, girls should ask themselves: what will I get out of this sexual contact that will be rewarding and beneficial to my life? Boys should ask themselves the same questions. The question should also be asked: what is the benefit, if any, for the other person involved? The teenage years are notoriously times of intense selfishness and self-preoccupation any- way, and this is how they should be. The transition from childhood to adulthood is a time of great change, both physical and mental, and there is often not much time or thought available for considering other people. Parents commonly sigh over their teenage children, and complain that they use the house like a hotel, that they expect shirts to be washed, rooms to be cleaned and underpants to appear magically in drawers without their owners ever offering to lend a hand with the washing up or tidy up their rooms. But the average teenager hardly realizes that other people exist, or that they have feelings. Teenagers are preoccupied with trying to work out their own attitudes to the world, and establish their own identity.

But perhaps the very greatest danger of entering into a sexual relationship too early is that it sets a pattern, if one is not very careful, for future behaviour. A teenage boy who is desperate for sex may never learn to become an unselfish man, but may grow up imagining that women exist just for his sexual pleasure. A girl who enters into sexual relationships too early in life may never learn how to become a person in her own right, and may spend the rest of her adulthood looking for somebody to lean on, feeling bereft if she does not have a relationship of some kind with a man – however unsatisfactory that relationship may be.

One lesson that adolescents could usefully learn along with their biology, English literature and chemistry is that physical sex can never solve any kind of personal problem. For too long teenagers have been fed the fantasy that sex with the right person will make all their troubles fade away. True, in the very early stages of a relationship this can seem to be the case, but before very long, responsibility has to be faced up to, and that for most young people is an unwanted extra burden. Any sexual involvement means that one has to take some kind of responsibility for the other person, to consider that individual and his or her needs.

Another drawback of having sexual relationships is that they tend to stop teenagers from forming other, non-sexual friendships. When one is always looking for that one, special person, others can be rejected as people because they are not considered sexually attractive. Celibacy – not necessarily as a lifelong commitment, but for those vital growing-up years – allows young people to be friendly in a relaxed way with a wide variety of others of the same age-group. A more relaxed atmosphere is engendered when people in a group know that their relationship is simply one of friends. All relationships can become more enjoyable and hassle-free when there is no possibility of sex being involved. Looking at teenagers, I would say that by far their happiest relationships are those that are not sexual. Those who have established a sexual attachment soon become discontented, dependent, clinging, possessive and suspicious of each other, stifling each other and each limiting their partner's freedom. Celibacy offers freedom where sex enslaves.

CHAPTER 5

Celibacy and women

The radical American feminist Andrea Dworkin once said in an interview: 'No woman needs intercourse. Few escape it.' Then later Germaine Greer stated in an article in the magazine *Woman's Own*: 'Women still see sex as a relatively unimportant part of an emotional complex. But for many women nowadays, sex is the only affection they get.' Germaine Greer went on to blame the contraceptive pill for making women available to men all the time.

Many modern women were horrified when they heard these pronouncements. What *could* these two famous feminists be getting at? Have we not all striven for sexual liberation, for the right and the opportunity to make love blessedly free from the fear of pregnancy, from moral censure and from the horror of a possible abortion? Have we not all learned to become sexually aggressive, to become the active instigators instead of the passive, reluctant recipients? May we not all be as lusty and as sexually free as men these days?

In hitting back at Dworkin and Greer, men – and women, it must be said – fell back on a traditional form of abuse and castigated these two women for looking frumpy, wearing dungarees, not wearing make-up and otherwise not taking the trouble to make themselves sexually attractive, to package themselves in a way that would be appealing to the average male.

The *Sunday Mirror* newspaper took particular exception to Dr Greer's pronouncements and invited a selection of celebrities to reassert what they felt we, as readers, wanted to hear – namely, that women wanted sex and were avid for as much as they could get. Barbara Windsor and Carroll Baker, two actresses now well into their fifties, said that their own sex lives were better than ever, and both added that they were of the opinion that sex improves, like good wine, with age. A marriage guidance counsellor named Zelda West-Meads was wheeled in to give her views, and she stated categorically: 'Women *do* want sex. They think it is fun and exciting.'

As a seasoned newspaper journalist myself, I know that it is common practice to exclude from the printed article any quotes which do not support the angle already decided upon. In this *Sunday Mirror* article only one quote was allowed – from a man – as 'balance'. This was from our old friend Dr Glenn Wilson, an amiable, bearded antipodean psychologist and amateur opera singer who has written several books on the nature of sexual attraction. He believes firmly that female sexual desire does not equal that of men, and that women tend to exert a restraining influence on male lust. He points to the extremely promiscuous behaviour of many male homosexuals, who do not have such restraints on their behaviour. Dr Wilson was quoted as saying: 'Men think of sex as fun while women think of love-making as symbolic.' In other words, Dr Wilson was saying that women are interested in sex only when there is already some form of emotional commitment to the other person. Sex for women when it is devoid of any feelings of love or attachment is not only not enjoyable, it becomes positively horrible.

Over the past twenty years, more or less since the pill became freely available, a certain proportion of women have clamoured for the right to regular, transcendental orgasms. This form of 'liberation' began in America, spread quickly to the UK and in time affected every suburban housewife. The average woman of a generation ago – our mothers' generation – on the whole never expected to enjoy sex but also, largely, accepted that men had dark and urgent needs that it was their duty to try to satisfy. If they did not, there was always the fear that the man in question would go off and find another woman who was more willing.

Our own generation, that is, those of us who were teenagers and young women in the 'sixties, expected and sought active sexual pleasure, and were disappointed if we did not experience it. Virginity, traditionally prized in a young girl, was seen as a millstone, something to be got rid of as quickly as possible. The model Jerry Hall – lover of pop star Mick Jagger and mother of two of his children – has related in several interviews how, at the age of 16, she asked a relative stranger to relieve her of the burden of her virginity. Mothers in the 'seventies who saw themselves as forward-thinking have declared publicly that they advised their 14-year-old daughters to go on the pill, have lovers and enjoy sex as much as possible. All this was seen as 'progress', as an essential part of our liberation from a repressive past in which we were only half alive.

The women's magazines of the 'seventies, notably *Cosmopolitan*, told women exactly how to achieve orgasms, and stressed in issue after issue how very important sex was to the modern girl. You were not, it was implied, a 'real' woman unless you had lots of sex with lots of different partners. In the past, men would triumphantly chalk up their conquests; now women could do the same. We could use men as they had always used us, to gratify our own sensual pleasure.

As the 'sexual revolution' progressed, anatomical observations seemed to confirm that women were actually far more like men than had ever previously been supposed. The vagina, which neatly accommodates most sizes of penis, and expands to allow a 10-pound baby through, is, to the regret of many sexual freedom-fighters, virtually devoid of sensation. Never mind, there is a minute knob of flesh somewhere down there called the clitoris which is abundantly supplied with nerve endings and which, like a penis, is capable of erection through sexual excitement. Indeed, it seems that the clitoris has no function apart from sexual pleasure. (Or would you call it pain? It depends, presumably, on who is administering the sensation.) Furthermore, diligent researchers in America found, in the mid-'seventies, another entity in the vagina which they termed the G, or Graefenberg, spot. Now this G-spot is capable not only of responding to excitement, but also produces a female ejaculate, much like a man's. So there you are, anatomy proves that we women are made to enjoy sex and lots of it. No longer need we be passive and timid and afraid. We too have sexual organs which are capable of both erection and ejaculation, just like a man's, only smaller and neater. So, we learned, there is absolutely no excuse. Take the initiative, we were advised, enjoy sex, have a good time, just as men have done throughout the centuries at our expense and pain.

Well, we tried. God, we tried. But somehow it didn't work. O.k., sex was all right for a bit and, truly, it could be the most sublime experience imaginable with a much-desired partner. But never did the bliss last, never did it add to the sum of happiness. Unless they constantly kept it to the forefront of their minds, the majority of women found they were in distinct danger of forgetting all about sex. Even when one is with the most fantastic man one has ever met, there is often a distinct feeling of disappointment when he starts indicating that he would like to be horizontal in the bedroom. Most women prefer to talk and exchange ideas, rather than waste time – as so many see it – groping around in messy body contact.

This is not to say women are incapable of sexual arousal. Of course they are, and one reason why romantic novels are the most popular reading matter everywhere in the world is that women can actually become physically aroused simply by fantasizing about making love with the handsome hero. Physical arousal can be an extremely pleasant sensation, in much the same way that cigarettes are pleasurable to smokers and wine or whisky are to drinkers. When adrenalin courses through the body, you can feel that you really are alive, pulsing with sensation.

The trouble is that, for all too many women nowadays, physical sex is the only – or at least the most vivid – sensation in a life which is otherwise dreary and mundane.

We are learning, however, to our cost, that sexual freedom and an active and varied sex life does not actually get us anywhere or enable us to achieve anything. Active involvement in, rather than passive endurance of, sexual intercourse, has not made women noticeably happier or more fulfilled. We have not become, since the sexual revolution, more equal, more achieving in the outside world. If anything, sex has worked against us by ruining our physical health and raising expectations that can never be met, because they are unmeetable. As nobody knows what amount of sexual desire, or libido, is supposed to be normal, or how it can best be satisfied, nobody can ever tell us how to arrive at maximum contentment and satisfaction in that area. We all know that there is no way of being turned back on by somebody who has long ceased to excite us sexually, whatever marriage guidance counsellors may say to the contrary.

Though the amount of physical arousal can now be accurately plotted on graphs, nobody can tell us why, after almost a quarter of a century of supposed sexual liberation, so many women remain dissatisfied and discontented, and are turning to drink and prescription drugs in ever-increasing quantities to blot out the emptiness they feel.

I have become convinced that women do not actually need sex, that they can live quite well without it, and that celibacy can be a far more life-enhancing and dignified way for a woman to behave than living from one sexual adventure to the next. In fact, it is really only over the past few years that women have actually had the choice as to whether or not they could be celibate, and we ought now to be taking advantage of that choice.

When most women were completely financially dependent on men, they had no option but to marry them and therefore to engage in sexual intercourse, for a marriage without sex could be annulled, and if the man left the woman she could then be in a sorry situation indeed. Those women who were not able to find a partner did, on the whole, remain celibate, but in most cases this would not have been by choice. The only women who consciously chose celibacy as a way of life were the very small number who were convinced they had a religious vocation. In the old days, getting oneself to a nunnery was the only honourable means of escaping sex.

When marriage was the only possible career for a woman, it was common to regard spinsters as 'frustrated'. This was not only because they were presumed to have no sexual outlet, but also because their lives would be even more circumscribed and poor than those of married women. Enforced celibacy is as bad as enforced sex: if a lack of choice is perceived, then health and possibly mental functioning will suffer.

But now, perhaps for the first time in history, women

do have a genuine choice in the matter of celibacy. So why are so few taking advantage of it? It is basically because we have not yet realized how truly liberating freedom from sexual involvement can be, and how consciously chosen celibacy is actually the *most* emancipated way of life there is.

By celibacy I do not mean monogamy, or 'saving oneself' for that special man in one's life. Nor am I placing a high value on virginity. As I see it, virginity is not the same as celibacy though it does, or can have, its own dynamic and is traditionally seen as conferring power on a woman. But perpetual virginity is now so rare that few women would be able to identify with the condition as a lifelong state.

Nor, when writing about celibacy, do I mean man-hating: rather the reverse, in fact. It is only when we can come to see the value of celibacy, the mental as well as the physical benefits, that we can actually start to relate to men as human beings, to stop being afraid of them and viewing them as the enemy, as beasts to be tamed. While we as women persist in seeing ourselves in the sexual mode, there is bound to be continuing hostility and fear between the sexes.

Those women who see themselves primarily as sexual creatures lose out in a variety of ways. First of all, they can never be independent or autonomous, because in order to satisfy sexual urges, another person has to be present. It is possible, of course, to 'satisfy' sexual desire by masturbation: Kinsey reported that more women had achieved orgasm this way than by penile penetration. But few would choose this as a way of life. Most women resort to self-satisfaction only after they have been left frustrated and miserable by an inept lover. For heterosexual women at least, the search is always on to find a good man, and this takes up an enormous amount of time and energy. Homosexual women hope to find a lasting lover of the same gender. Either way, there is a danger that your happiness will become dependent on the whims and personality of another, who may not be around at the right time, who may not feel like sex when you do, or who may feel like sex when you do not, or who may himself, or herself, for some reason, want to force or withhold sex.

Wherever there is a sexual relationship, there is bound, at times, to be hostility. Desire and satisfaction, which are different for every individual, can never coincide, at least not on a long-term basis. Quarrels and tensions are bound to build up, however loving and compatible a couple you may have seemed to be at first.

Then, while a woman continues to think of herself as a sexual being, she will waste a lot of time worrying about whether her body is in good shape, whether her clothes are fashionable enough, whether she is attractive enough, whether, as she gets older, she is losing her looks. She will also worry about how she competes with other women in the sexual market-place. This does not mean to say that women should not make themselves look attractive and aesthetically pleasing. Though I would call myself a feminist, I emphatically do not go along with the no-make-up-and-dungarees-hairy-armpits-take-me-as-I-am school of thought. I believe in the value of harmony and pretty, co-ordinating clothes, rather than disharmony and confusion in dress. Complementary colours, fashionable, clean clothes, shining well-cut hair and attention to accessories convey to me a sense of self-confidence and self-worth. They do not have to say, 'I am sexually available.' An attractive appearance simply announces to the world that you consider yourself worth taking time and trouble over.

There is no need at all for celibate women to look ungainly or unattractive, as some people believe. It is a mistake to imagine that sexuality automatically confers attractiveness, or that you will suddenly start growing a moustache, or becoming bald, if you are not sexually active. The decision to be celibate does not make a woman less physically attractive: rather the reverse, for as self-confidence increases you feel cleaner and more in control of yourself. There is no fear of pregnancy or of sex-related disease, or of the possibility that a lover may go off you and find somebody new. The removal of all these burdens can act to bring about a glow of inner peace, vitality and confidence. When you decide to remove sex from your life, you remove at the same time a potent source of anxiety, illness and depression.

Celibate women do not have to go out of their way to

repel the male sex; they simply stop relating to men in a sexual way. When women can stop thinking of themselves primarily as sexual beings, they become less timid and less afraid when in male company. There is a line in Milton's poem 'Comus' about chastity: 'She that has it is clad in complete steel.' What he means here is that chastity gives protection in some way. After taking the decision to become celibate, women no longer fear rapes or sexual attacks to the same extent. It is a well-known psychological truth that if you fear something happening, in a subtle way you actually increase the possibility of it happening. Women do not want to be raped, but they want to attract men. Therefore, while they regard themselves as sexual beings, they are putting out confused signals about themselves.

Physical attacks such as rape are far less likely to happen when you are no longer putting out the combined vibrations of sexuality and fear. Those who teach self-defence know that, the more self-confident and unafraid people are, the more this will show in their whole manner. Until recently, many women who reported rape were traditionally accused of 'asking for it' or, by their demeanour, consenting to it. This 'asking for it' was often taken by judges as a complete defence. If a woman, at the time of the rape, wore a short skirt, a low-cut dress, or false eyelashes, or was out after midnight, she could be presumed to have 'consented', in some way, to the rape. Though feminists and radical-thinking people are rightly horrified that a woman should be presumed to want, or to welcome, physical abuse, what they have in general failed to recognize is that insistence on a woman's right to sexual fulfilment and the rising rape figures go hand in hand.

Once when I was writing an article about the terrible rise in rape cases I asked the staff at a Rape Crisis Centre whether they saw any connection between the new centrality of sex in women's lives and the rape figures. They were thunderstruck and disconcerted. No, they said emphatically, adding that they were convinced the rise in rape was entirely due to the lack of late-night transport and safe housing for women who might be at risk. The fact that in over 50 per cent of cases rapists are well known to their victims did not shake them of this conviction. Yet a confused man cannot be expected to know the difference between a woman who wants it and one who does not. By insisting that we are sexual creatures, we have, in some way, invited ourselves to be raped. Sexual intercourse is fundamentally and necessarily a violent act, and whether you call it rape or making love simply depends on the circumstances at the time. When people first marry their desire may be equal and they may consider their acts of intercourse making love. After some years, when desire has waned, the man may try to force his wife, and intercourse might then be classed as rape. How is the man to know? Does the woman even know herself, always, whether any particular act of intercourse is rape or love-making? Is there really any difference?

When women describe sexual experiences with a wanted lover, they commonly say how 'gentle' the man was. In saying this they are, of course, implying the complete opposite. Unless there is some degree of physical violence sexual intercourse simply cannot take place. Unless there is some element of force, the man's penis cannot penetrate the vagina, even when the vagina is ready to accept it.

If a man takes a woman against her will, then intercourse is considered rape. If the woman has instigated it, it is making love. Yet the mechanics of the act are identical, whatever distinctions the mind may be making at the time. Often in romantic fiction the hero, unable to contain himself, rips off the heroine's blouse, then the rest of her clothes, and makes love to her despite her protestations, knowing full well that she really 'wants it'. When we read romantic fiction and identify with the heroine, we too fantasize about being made love to by a handsome hulk.

Authors of books that examine the question of rape often agonize over the possibility that a woman who has been raped will not then want to have a 'normal' sex life afterwards, as if this were some kind of deprivation. Women interviewed after being raped have commonly said that it took them years to get over the experience, and that they did not want to have sex again, no matter who the man or what the relationship. These authors do not define, as there is no definition, what is meant by a 'normal sex life', or state precisely how a raped woman's life may subsequently be enhanced by a certain level of sexual intercourse.

What most writers of books on rape do not envisage is the possibility of a non-sexual life for the victim after the violent act of rape. Their books reinforce the idea which has become orthodox in our thinking that women actually want the 'right' sort of sex. This thinking really started with Freud, who held that women basically wanted sex all the time, and when they did not get it, they fantasized about it. He has on record many cases of patients who supposedly fantasized instances of incest and other forms of sexual abuse. Recently, however, some new evidence is leading us to re-examine Freud's theories. It seems now that many, if not all, of these cases were actual case histories, not fantasies.

Dr Jeffrey Masson, a Freudian scholar from Berkeley, California, author of *The Assault on Truth: Freud's Suppression of the Seduction Theory*, argues that Freud deliberately misrepresented the cases of women who had come to him for treatment. So shocking were Dr Masson's findings that he has since been shunned by his profession. What Dr Masson argues, from a meticulous examination of Freud's papers, was that having uncovered horrific cases of sexual abuse of women, Freud then had to cover them up by pretending they were all fantasies, to avoid damaging his career. In saying that outwardly respectable men perpetrated sexual abuse on their daughters, wives and other relatives Freud was voicing the unspeakable and unimaginable, and he knew it. He had to turn fact into fantasy. The papers proving this remained hidden for many years. For over half a century, women have been credited with shameful sexual feelings that they did not have. Most psychoanalysts today, following Freud, believe that women who come to them with stories of sexual abuse are usually fantasizing.

In a *Guardian* interview Dr Masson, commenting on the storm that followed publication of his book, said: 'Not one analyst has called or written to discuss my book or agreed to take part in debates . . . They are reacting not as analysts but as *men*, because here we are touching on the last taboo, the most shameful secret of all, the male secret. All the favourable letters I have received came from women, hundreds, saying that their analysts refused to believe their stories of abuse, or that it was relevant.' Instead, it seems, the analysts would ask each woman 'what she did to seduce her father.'

It appears that women were cruelly misrepresented by Freud as vapid, fantasizing creatures full of unexpressed sexuality, who were out to seduce and ensnare men – even men who were their own fathers or in some other way related. The new evidence now emerging shows that Freud really knew what was happening but to protect his career suppressed the evidence and disguised fact as the disordered workings of a hysterical mind.

Dr Masson's findings about Freud have, he claims, turned him into a radical feminist. When Freud's complete papers are finally allowed to be published – in the year 2020 – we shall know for certain how many real cases of rape and sexual abuse by close relatives Freud was able to examine. Already there are far-reaching implications for our view of female sexuality.

Our understanding, or misunderstanding, of Freud's theories has led all of us, men and women alike, to believe that all women are inherently sexual creatures, whose lives would be empty and meaningless without sex. This has happened largely because we have confused sex with love, and have imagined that the two must go together. The 'agony aunt' Irma Kurtz has said, *à propos* of romantic fiction: 'Every Mills and Boon story projects the idea that sex strengthens love. Few women find this in real life.' Sex cannot even begin to strengthen love because it has simply nothing to do with love. In fact, there can be more genuine love through celibacy than is ever possible through sex, because if you truly love a person you will be most interested in what is best for him or her, rather than the satisfaction of your own desires.

Many women fear becoming celibate because they do not wish to forfeit the experience of warm physical contact with other human beings. They worry that if they say goodbye to sex they will be losing out on other physical expressions of affection, such as hugs, kisses and cuddles, all of which are usually seen as pleasurable. But one has to ask: are these genuine expressions of affection, or are they simply a temporary return to an infantile state? Among those who feel that we are missing out by not touching each other in an affectionate way are the American therapist Ashley Montague and Dr Leo Buscaglia – a bachelor, and author of many books on the importance of physical contact. They claim we have become afraid of touching, and we go out of our way to avoid each other.

Most people find that once they are adult the only affection they get is through sex, and they have come to associate the one with the other. But do we as adults really need to be hugged by other people? Is that so big a deal? Desmond Morris, the anthropologist, has called cuddling and hugging 'infantile', and so they are. Babies need to be hugged and cuddled, as do small children, but does a 40-year-old woman? Why do people feel that affection must always be demonstrated in physical ways? After all, it does not necessarily mean anything.

The only people I ever want to hug are members of my own family, and close friends. In these cases, hugging is an outward sign of mental and emotional closeness, but if I do not receive hugs from my family, I do not feel deprived. It is not that I'm after hugs *per se*. To me, there is no pleasure whatever in being hugged by a stranger. If there is no member of my family to give or receive hugs, I do not, and nor, I suspect, does anybody else, go around in an agony of longing to be hugged. This physical act only ever means something when it is performed by one who is *already* loved and dear. It does not strengthen a bond, or forge one where there was none before.

In fact, it is the celibate woman who is likely to gain *more* hugs and kisses, if she so wishes, because she will never be afraid that a demonstration of affection will lead to sex or other unwelcome advances. A man who knows that a certain woman is celibate will respect that. Already, he will be a little in awe of her.

Sex, for women as well as men, is rarely an expression of affection. It may appear so at first, but before long it will be the cause of dissension rather than a spontaneous expression of love. What we often fail to realize is that the phallus is actually a weapon, and will, in any heterosexual relationship, eventually be used as a means of domination. Male power, as many feminists have pointed out, usually comes to be the central problem within any man/woman relationship. If we think about it, most definitions of what constitutes 'normal' sexuality have come from men – Freud, Alex Comfort, Havelock Ellis, Kinsey – all the so-called sex experts – and in all the definitions the male organ has assumed a primary role. Men, all too often encouraged by women in their belief, have come to believe that they have a right to women's bodies, and that it is natural for a man to put pressure on a woman to have sex with him. Almost all women, at least in the Western world, have at some time or other been subject to male pressure for sex. Very often, this coercion comes from a lover, husband or boyfriend who is supposed to be fond of them. While we continue to regard ourselves as sexual entities, we will start to feel guilty if we have appeared to encourage a man, dressed provocatively or said 'No' when he believes we mean yes.

All too many women grow up thinking that men have sexual rights over them and that it is wrong to refuse them. Large numbers of women who are married deliberately set out to make themselves unattractive so that their husbands will not bother them. In a questionnaire sent to 200 readers of the feminist magazine *Spare Rib*, most respondents admitted that they did not enjoy sex very much. Yet few imagined they could do without it, or that the men in their lives would allow this state of affairs. It can take a very long time, and a huge amount of self-confidence, for a woman to realize that she has no obligation whatever to meet a man's sexual demands.

The feminist writer Deborah Gregory stated in an essay entitled 'A Case for Feminist Bisexuality' an uncomfortable truth that will strike a chord with many women, even those who protest that they are not feminists. She writes: 'Many women find penetration by a penis oppressive and humiliating, and refuse to do it. Some [women] have mentioned a dislike of semen, or a dislike of available contraception.'

In an essay entitled 'Women Alone', another feminist writer, Tricia Bickerton, drew attention to the fact that women can choose to be unsexual, if they like, because men are no longer as necessary as they were to women's economic survival. This in itself is enabling us to change our views about sexuality. 'Is adult desire,' Tricia Bickerton asks, 'reducible to women's socially-determined dependency on men?' She continues: 'A sexual relationship provides women with very little sense of their own identity. For this reason, it is often a positive experience for a woman to be alone, without a sexual partner . . . she becomes stronger.'

I am convinced that there can never be true equality between the sexes while there is a sexual ingredient in a relationship. Sex inevitably brings about possessiveness, and through sex we can come to feel that we entirely possess the other person. In most sexual relationships neither partner is allowed to have sex with anybody else; if this does happen, love will instantly turn to hate and bitterness.

Men on the whole do not like the thought of women becoming celibate, because this deprives them of their primary means of control over the opposite sex. A woman who is celibate by choice becomes a powerful woman. By becoming celibate she is saying in effect that she does not want intimate bodily contact in the genital area to be her primary means of relating to other people. A celibate woman soon finds she has more friends, as she has more time to establish proper relationships with a large circle of people. She can be truly equal with a man when there is no question of any kind of sexual liaison with him.

In relinquishing sex, a woman does not become cold-hearted, distant or 'frustrated'; it can in fact make her warmer-hearted and happier because at a stroke it relieves her of a major source of worry and anxiety, a drain on her physical, mental and emotional powers. She will find that she becomes more creative, that her true identity can start to assert itself.

Instead of effort being directed downwards, with energy being diverted into devising ever more exotic sexual routines, it can be channelled into autonomous, worthwhile pursuits. A celibate woman can have more energy for the things that matter to her, and her alone. If you think about it, sex takes up a great deal of time in most women's lives – and for what end result? What happens at the end of the day except acrimony and bad feeling?

There is a growing feeling among certain feminists that the current idea that women are all desperate for regular sex – a fallacy for which Freud, as we have seen, was largely responsible – has already removed a considerable degree of choice from our lives and added one more burden. In the book *Love and Sex*, a compilation of articles on the subject written by various feminists, editors Sue Cartledge and Joanna Ryan write: 'The break with chastity as old-fashioned meant the removal of the unmarried woman's right to say no. The pressure on women to have intercourse has increased ... In the 1960s, the final denigration of chastity and the right of unmarried women to reject male advances was also lost.'

Lynne Segal, a contributor to the book, writes: 'With sexual pleasure, we were disappointed more often than not.' Lynne Segal concludes her essay with the remark: 'What is wrong with our lives is not so much the lack of orgasm as our perpetual craving for that orgasm, which can obliterate the isolation and emptiness we feel in the rest of our lives.'

One does not have to be a radical feminist to realize the truth of these statements. The busier, happier and more useful and creative a woman feels, the less she will hunger and thirst after some fantasy sexual satisfaction. The more sense of purpose, self-esteem and confidence she can have within herself the less she will concern herself with the fundamental emptiness of the search for transcendence and closeness through sex. Instead of devoting energies to establishing relationships that will always go wrong, she will be able to devote time to getting to know herself, to becoming strong and self-sufficient. The search for self-knowledge and autonomy is a far more rewarding one than the search for sexual satisfaction, and, unlike sex, there are guaranteed positive results.

In our present society few women – apart from those with a religious vocation – ever even consider becoming celibate. Those few who have 'come out' in this manner always talk about the benefits, never the drawbacks. But in so doing, they very often feel they have to apologize for their behaviour, as it is not considered normal.

In a letter to *Over 21* a magazine for young women, a correspondent said:

Just recently I finished a relationship with a boy who I thought really cared. Why? Because I decided to become celibate for a while and give my body a rest. Also I have been on the pill since I was 16 (I'm now 22) and I feel that my body doesn't deserve to be filled with chemicals to mess up the hormones . . . Another reason is because I don't feel sex is very important at the moment and friendship is. After having explained all this and giving him the option to back out first, he accepted, then added: "If this goes on for longer than a month, then maybe you ought to see someone about it." How dare he treat me as some frigid woman, just because I have decided to abstain from sex for a while?

An older woman, Diana Eden, decided to become celibate at the age of 38, and wrote an article in *The Guardian* about her decision. Again, she explains that she was considered decidedly odd. In the course of her article, Diana Eden stated that her celibacy had originally been forced on her by circumstances, after her second marriage broke up, but that gradually she came to realize there were definite benefits she had not previously imagined. Admitting that men immediately start to make 'availability checks' once they learn a reasonably attractive woman is divorced, she goes on to say:

Celibacy . . . is often regarded as a form of social leprosy. And many people find it difficult to comprehend that the condition could possibly be one of choice. Surely *someone* must have offered to go to bed with you? one aghast chauvinist exclaimed.

She continues:

The constraints of chastity also bring other attendant liberties. What matters now the grubby bra? Who passes searing judgement on my bedside books? . . . Since aggressively "coming out" as celibate, others of the same persuasion have sheepishly owned up . . . We are not, contrary to frequently received opinion, frigid, frightened or sexually shy.

In writing this article Diana Eden was being courageous, swimming against the tide of opinion which says we must have sex, otherwise we will wither away and become non-humans. Half a century ago, it would have been shocking for a single woman of whatever age to admit to having an active sex life. Now we recoil in disbelief when we hear that a pre-menopausal woman has become celibate from choice.

A few years ago an American academic, Martha Allen, launched a small-budget journal called *The Celibate Woman*. She explained to disbelievers, who wondered how there could possibly be a market for such a magazine, why she decided to found it.

Here is her manifesto:

While most of us spend a portion of our lives in a celibate state, we are not always able to appreciate its benefits when all around us there is an attitude that the only healthy and happy way to live one's life is to be sexually active. If one does not have a partner with whom a sexual relationship can be shared, one is expected to seek a partner. Otherwise one's life is not considered to be "full" or "complete".

Yet, at the same time, more of us are discovering that choosing celibacy can be a very positive choice and that this lifestyle can provide healthier and happier relationships with those we care about, including those with whom we share an intimate relationship. Living in a society where sex enters practically every aspect of our lives, it is refreshing to share new ideas, to explore new ways of relating to others.

As one woman expressed in the first issue of the journal, "What made celibacy possible for me was the realization that it does not mean giving up affection and touching. What it means for me is not taking affection in a sexual direction. In fact, I find that when I do not narrow my affection by taking it sexually, I experience more equal and warm relationships with everyone I care about." Another wrote in "One Year of Celibacy" that during that year she had more relationships, both personal and professional, and more affection than at any other time in her life. Still another woman expressed that when sex enters a relationship, the friendship part suffers. In an interview in the first issue, two women agreed that the negative aspect of a sexual involvement, other than disrupting a friendship, is that the sexual relationship or sexual experience does not always proceed as you imagine it would. You may think you want the sexual dimension, one woman noted, "But what you really want is your fantasy, the way you wish it would be." These and other reflections on celibacy and sexuality are increasingly shared and articulated, promoting the creation of new forms of interpersonal relationships.

One may wonder: is celibacy only for the extraordinary, the special woman, one who has a burning desire to achieve something in the world, rather than something which has benefits for everybody? I believe that if more women became celibate, more could become special. A sexual relationship is confining, restricting and limiting to the intelligence. In fact, just to be celibate, just to make that personal decision, in itself makes a woman special. It means you are saying to yourself: I am important, I matter and I will not allow my body to be defiled and used by another person for momentary gratification. Nor will I attempt to use another person's body in this way.

It is up to women to show the way in celibacy. We cannot expect men to do this unless they have decided for some reason that they will exercise self-control in this area. I do believe that it is far harder for a man than a woman to be celibate. This is not because men have sexual urges they cannot control – although there is an element of this – so much as that they equate sex with being powerful, with being dominant. I shall explain why I think this in the chapter on celibacy and men.

Andrea Dworkin explains why she feels it is up to women to lead the way in promoting the positive side of celibacy: 'Until we understand this social system we are dealing with, we are just going to go on asking men to be nice to us . . . Until we understand it, we're going to go on being Sue Ellen saying, "Please, JR, not again, JR." '

We have to learn to understand that a man who demands sex is not worth giving in to, that he has no right whatever, whether he is lover, boyfriend or husband, to assume he can have access to our bodies whenever he wishes. A man who demands sex does not really care for the woman from whom he is demanding this favour.

We have to learn to become less frightened of men, to realize that if we refuse them sex they are not going to go out and rape children or commit some terrible crime. We must help men realize that the celibate life has great benefits for them as well. But before this can happen, before women can once again exercise control over what happens to their own bodies, we have to become stronger and more grown-up in ourselves, and not seek physical manifestations of affection. This is important. Women have to learn not to want to be hugged and kissed all the time, and hence, prepared to put up with sex as the price for affection. In a non-sexual society, perhaps, hugs would not be regarded as the preliminary to sex, but nowadays they often are.

Celibacy, we realize once we have decided to embrace this condition, frees the mind, and frees us from the last vestiges of dependence on men. While we as women continue to speak about our sexuality, and our sexual needs, we can never expect respect from men. They will continue to regard us as sexually voracious, emasculating temptresses, leading them astray. In our present society, such is the insistence on physical attractiveness of women that a woman not perceived as attractive is marked down, by both men and women, as an inferior human being.

We know in our hearts that, as women, we are not really all that interested in sex. A survey in the magazine *True Romances*, conducted and published in 1986, discovered that the lack of interest in physical sex is as great as ever, despite the continuing avalanche of sex manuals and articles on the subject. Making love with a regular partner came third on the list of preferred intimate activities undertaken by readers, a long way after kissing and cuddling and talking. Only five per cent of the respondents said that being a 'sensational lover' was important in a man, whereas 'a best friend' came far and away top of the list.

About 75 per cent of women said they were 'seriously involved' with the man to whom they first made love. The survey revealed that the mythical average woman is certainly not eager for sex, but instead likes friendship, a close companion and a caring partner. Unfortunately, in our sex-obsessed society, though she may seek all these things from a relationship with a man, she rarely finds them. So desperate are women for this close relationship that they imagine being sexual and available will bring them the closeness they desire.

The sexual revolution has sold women very short. By putting ever more emphasis on bodies and couplings, and exotic sexual activity, we are draining ourselves of energy, of our sense of self and of our individuality. We are losing much while gaining very little of positive value. The rewards of believing that sex can solve deep-seated problems and yearnings are only ill health, unhappiness and even more frustration.

When I interviewed her recently, Martha Allen, the founder of the journal *Celibate Woman*, said: 'Because of today's over-emphasis on sex, many women feel they have no choice but to be sexually involved in order to feel fulfilled. I believe that pressure to have sexual relationships can actually hinder an independent outlook.' Stressing that she was not advocating lifelong, perpetual celibacy for everybody, Martha Allen added: 'Then when you do become involved again, it is from proper choice rather than perceived need.' Martha said that very many women had written to say how they welcomed the journal, and that they had not previously realized they actually could make the choice not to be sexual.

One last point: very many women hate and are ashamed of their bodies. Consequently, a huge industry has grown up advising women how they can lose weight, have softer, smoother skin, have the fat surgically removed from their thighs, have breast augmentation or reduction, face-lifts, hair coloured and permed – all so that they can continue to be sexually attractive. Apart from being better for health both physical and mental, celibacy is also cheaper. You no longer have to worry about whether your body is pleasing to men, and therefore do not have to spend time and money on preparations on trying to make yourself into a fantasy female. Women who choose celibacy cease to hate their bodies so much. Henceforward, they are not going to be judged on whether their particular arrangement of flesh and bones is sexually a turn-on. Once they no longer have to worry about such matters, many women discover a new inner happiness.

In every way you can imagine, celibacy improves a woman's life.

CHAPTER 6

Celibacy and men

It is commonly believed that the average non-geriatric man is physically incapable of going without sex for any length of time. America's favourite media therapist, Dr Joyce Brothers, claimed in her book *What Every Woman Should Know About Men* that most males think about sex six times an hour and dream about sex at least three times as often as women. Just about every man there is, according to Dr Brothers, appraises all women sexually and speculates how each one would perform in bed, however remote from reality this may be.

In a recent article in the radical magazine *New Internationalist*, a left-wing publication, celibacy was mentioned as a valid contraceptive option only for women. The idea was expressed that men were constitutionally incapable of celibacy, and would not even begin to consider this as a sensible contraceptive measure. It seems that, in spite of strenuous attempts to equalize male and female sexuality, the stereotype remains unchanged. Men want sex, demand sex, and say they cannot live without it, whereas women are, by and large, indifferent, as the previous chapter has proposed.

How true is all this? Are men really more sexually inclined, more likely than women to see sex as absolutely central to their lives? Certainly it is the case that almost all sex crimes are committed by men, who also sexually abuse children, commit incest and have homosexual liaisons.

It is also men who commit rape. Indeed, it is hard to see how a woman could possibly rape a man. Some years ago, in a celebrated British court case, an attractive young American woman, Joyce MacKinney, was accused of tying a celibate Mormon, Kirk Anderson, to a bedpost and forcing him to have sex with her. In her evidence, the woman asked how an 8-stone woman could rape a 15-

stone man against his will. Much of the interest in this case focused on just how she could have achieved this unlikely feat. There was not all that much sympathy for the young Mormon male, pledged to chastity while unmarried. Most men on reading the story felt it fulfilled their wildest fantasies – that a *woman* should actually want to force a *man* into having sex. All too often, it is the other way round.

In real life, most men find that their penises are not wildly in demand. Most women do not like them very much and in fact remain rather frightened of them. Men involved in a heterosexual relationship often discover that, before very long, they have to use persuasion to get their female partner to agree to sex. Even when the sex urge has been equal to begin with, in most women it recedes dramatically after a year or so, unless a new relationship is started. When a woman is first in love, a man may have difficulty in keeping up with her ardour. If he expects this to continue throughout many years, however, he will soon be sadly disappointed.

After a time, however torrid the affair may have been at first, indifference will prevail in the woman. She will actually start to forget about sex, and find it a chore. So it certainly seems that, on the face of it, men are the more sexually-inclined sex. They are the buyers of pornographic magazines and the oglers of female nudes. There is not a corresponding market in male nudes for women; most buyers of magazines featuring naked men are male homosexuals. Women find it intensely boring to look at one picture after another of male bodies. For a man, of course, the scenario is different. He finds looking at female bodies constantly exciting, because he can weave fantasies around them.

We also assume that men are more sexual because they appear to have greater difficulty in keeping celibate, even when they may, for religious or other reasons, have to do this. We have heard how early Christian saints were tormented by visions of dancing girls, and felt they had to resort to scourging the flesh to resist temptation. Mahatma Gandhi, who embraced lifelong celibacy at the age of 36, continued to be bothered by sexual thoughts, and very late in life embarked on a series of celibacy experiments in which he would sleep with young women to prove to himself that he had conquered bodily desires. As he was 77 years old at the time, one wonders how on earth he coped during his previous 40 years of self-imposed celibacy.

One also wonders what the women who agreed to sleep with Gandhi gained from the experience. Was their sexual desire considered important, or not? Did they have any such desire? At any rate, there seemed to be no shortage of willing females, even though Gandhi was hardly a romantic hero, being very old, skeletal and toothless at the time. He did have, of course, that elusive quality many men seek and few possess – charisma.

Throughout the ages, it has been considered 'holier' for men than women to be celibate. It is assumed they have more to give up and more urgent desires to overcome. In relinquishing the sex urge to follow some higher ideal, many men still find themselves disturbed by the memory of the sexual act. It appears that the longer they have engaged in sexual practices, the longer the habit takes to go away, or to cease to be bothersome. One writer, the feminist theologian Mary Daly, has called much of male celibacy 'phallic asceticism'. For men, she argues, it is often just the reverse side of the sexual coin, involving as much ego and desire for power as when the sex organ is being employed.

Catholic priests excite fascination and wonderment from the non-celibate. A potent ingredient of Colleen McCullough's best-selling book *The Thorn Birds* is a handsome, clever and ambitious hero who is also a celibate Catholic priest. He has succumbed once and only once, with important consequences for the plot. The one question people long to ask of celibate priests is: don't you miss sex? The popular belief has been that religious celibate males are sexually frustrated almost the entire time, and if they do not masturbate regularly, or otherwise manage to sublimate their physical urges, they are in distinct danger of going mad. In fact, most men who have embraced the religious life do not continue to find the absence of sex a problem. The reason is that they have decided to live in a different way from the rest of the world and are concentrating their thoughts on non-material matters. Also, most usually, they withdraw from the world to live in celibate communities.

Men who continue to live a full and active life in the outside world, such as Gandhi, may find it more difficult to become celibate. Gandhi, like so many men before him, tended to see women as temptation to which he must not yield.

Many men would sympathize with the idea of becoming celibate in order to reach a higher ideal, but few who are living ordinary lives can easily see the point of giving up sex. Why relinquish one of the greatest sources of pleasure in life? For the majority of men today, sex is seen as synonymous with good living; those with active and varied sex lives are among the most envied. One tends to feel sorry for the celibate, and concerned with what he or she is missing. Also, men to whom sex is important are usually regarded as more 'masculine' than those who have a low sex drive. So much is masculinity seen to be allied to the sex drive that those men who are not very interested in sex are often regarded as figures of fun.

For several years there was a popular comedy series on British television called *George and Mildred*. Much of the humour in the series lay in the fact that George had a very low sex drive and was, by implication, a complete doormat in every other aspect of his life. He was entirely dominated by Mildred, who was – or would have been, given the chance – a very sexy lady. George's lack of interest in sex made him seem feeble, unassertive, unattractive.

By contrast, the successful characters in Harold Robbins novels have an almost permanent erection. Robbins' obsession with the mechanics of the male genitalia have earned him a fortune. His novels have so far sold over 260 million copies and *every week* 280,000 people – most of them men – buy a Harold Robbins book.

In an article in *Literary Review*, the critic Paul Taylor, commenting on the success of the Robbins formula, observed: 'The narrative method of the world's greatest storyteller is sublimely simple and consists in finding the shortest possible line between two gargantuan hard-ons.' In one of Robbins' later novels, *The Storyteller*, a struggling young writer is sitting in his underpants tapping out a rape scene. He is observed by a young woman entering the room who cannot help noticing that he has a huge erection. She asks how he can possibly carry on writing with such an enormous bulge, and he tells her that he has to feel everything he writes. When he writes about fear, he says, he feels afraid, when he writes about weeping, he cries, and when he writes about sex, naturally, he has an erection. Paul Taylor went on to wonder what happened when he wrote crap.

In the average Harold Robbins novel – though not of course in real life – the women do little else but admire the men's erections, and love nothing more than engaging in orgasmic and exotic sex with these characters. No doubt that is why his books are so universally popular – if only, men dream, women were like that in reality! The novels trade in potent male fantasies, in which the hero forever has a hard-on and droves of sex-hungry, compliant women line up to worship and adore the erect penis.

Of course, what all this insistence on sex is really about is gaining power, rather than any desperate, uncontrollable urge to release long-pent-up semen. Paul Taylor writes *à propos* of the typical Harold Robbins hero: 'In all the novels, the heroes exult in the single-minded control of their destinies, yet cannot practise the most minimal sexual restraint.' For most males, however, sexual penetration *is* control. A man who is always trying to have sexual intercourse with women is not simply over-endowed with sexual appetite: most of all, he wants to have domination over women. By implication, the erect male organ is used to control the world. The American novelist Marilyn French has observed wonderingly that the sex which cannot even control its own sex organ should imagine it has a right to control the world. But the male organ is seen as a means of control, and is used as such.

As Ms French observes in her latest book, *Beyond Power: Men, Women and Morals*, the male desire is to exercise control over other people and over the environment, rather than trying to work in harmony. The weapon that men have used to try to exert this control is the erect penis, or its symbolic manifestations.

One thinks of Concorde, the Empire State Building, the Eiffel Tower, nuclear warheads, space rockets. The phallus goes everywhere, controlling everything. The paradox is that most of nature is incapable of such control. Women cannot really be controlled by sex: they become restive and start to complain. Mother Earth fails to yield up riches and everything soon goes madly out of control. The Russian nuclear plant disaster at Chernobyl is an example of this: the radiation cannot be contained, and nobody knows where it will end, or how many years it will take before all dangerous radiation levels are reduced.

As women, nature and nuclear weapons go so easily out of control, so does the male organ go out of control. When sex becomes over-important to a man, out of all proportion to other activities, the male organ takes on a life of its own and starts to control the man, the sentient being.

This phenomenon has been observed in a series of extremely amusing – and hot-selling – cartoon books by Gray Joliffe and Peter Mayle, called *Man's Best Friend*, where the willie is depicted as a thinking being in its own right. In the novel *Lady Chatterley's Lover*, the gamekeeper Mellors observes that the penis has a life and will of its own. Sir Clifford Chatterley, Lady C's husband, is impotent and disabled and therefore, in Lawrentian terms, not really a man at all. As he is unable to use his sex organ, he cannot 'control' his wife, who naturally enough goes off with another man.

Over the past 30 years, there has been a greater focus on male sexuality than at any other time in history. It started in America and is neatly chronicled in Gay Talese's book *Thy Brother's Wife*. Talese charts how male sexuality gradually came out of the bedroom and into big-business boardrooms. Today, the men's magazines *Playboy*, *Penthouse* and *Hustler*, plus their derivatives, have a combined circulation of about 25 million copies an issue. Female sexuality came out too, as a byproduct, but it is the pandering to male sexuality which sells and sells and sells. The fantasy male of today, as epitomized in the James Bond films, is in total control. Single-handedly he fights and wins every battle, whether in a train compartment, a boardroom, an underground hangar, a lake full of man-eating crocodiles, or underwater – in all these places, it seems, there are evil men who want to take over the world. In each case, the sex organ is always ready to be fully operational, and the fantasy man's reward for winning yet again is a beautiful girl in his bed – a different one every time. Whenever James Bond emerges (always unscathed) from his hair-raising adventures, he 'celebrates' with a bottle of champagne in a bucket – another potent phallic symbol – and a new sexual adventure. Most of these fantasy situations involve a blonde, and gentlemen do prefer them, claims the psychiatrist Dr Roderic Gorney, because in the make-believe world inhabited by so many men, blondes combine the innocent sweetness of childhood with the mature sexuality of which no child is capable.

The sexual male, always ready to be fully erect, is in charge, dominating women and 'satisfying' them, taming them with his organ. James Bond uses sex to tame wild women – and it always succeeds. They melt before him. This fantasy is potent with women as well, as the vast sales of romantic novels bear witness. But in neither Harold Robbins nor Ian Fleming fantasies do men ever interact with women on any level other than the sexual one. They are not interested in females as multi-dimensional human beings, but only as a 'piece of pussy' or a 'burning cunt', as Harold Robbins delicately puts it.

This attitude does not, as we shall see, bode at all well for male/female relationships, nor does it ultimately make men happy, as they are continuously in search of something which can never be brought about. More often than not, in real life, men become deeply dissatisfied, hurt, and both disappointed and confused by sex: why, they wonder, aren't real women all pulsating with desire and ready to drop their knickers, as they are in fantasy fiction.

Many men could become far happier if they added the positive benefits of celibacy to their lives. But in our sex-saturated society, it is hard for them to realize this and difficult for them to break this potent addiction.

An interesting book by a Frenchman, Emmanuel Reynaud, analyses the reality of male sexuality. Called *Holy Virility*, the book explains how and why men have taken a sexually dominant position in the world. Reynaud says it is mainly because power is, for a man, concentrated at the tip of the phallus. When a man is sexually operational, he can impose femininity on a woman. The more a man restricts and controls the freedom and well-being of women, the more he feels in control of his own body. According to Reynaud, the male has, over the centuries, covered the earth with phalluses which increase in height and projectability all the time. Nuclear warheads are the ultimate example.

The erect penis, Reynaud goes on to say, is a weapon that any man can have, and he arms himself with this to try to tame the women in his life, through the woman's vagina. He tries to make the penis threatening and arouse fear, and certainly when confronted with rape women are afraid of the male organ. Even long-married women may remain somewhat in awe of the penis when they see it rising and growing to more than twice its quiescent size.

Most men at some time in their sexual lives will try to impose themselves sexually on women. This is seen in the young man's traditional lament to his reluctant girlfriend: if you really loved me, you would sleep with me. Youths of 17 and 18 still wish as fervently as the young men of previous generations that girls would not impose rules and restrictions and insist on certain conditions before they will allow penetration. The same attitude is also seen in the slightly older man's complaint: you're supposed to be liberated now, he says to a reluctant woman; you're supposed to enjoy it now. This imposition is so time-honoured we have come to consider it as normal and natural, but actually it is rape by another name.

Emmanuel Reynaud observes: 'Men imagine their sperm permanently marks a woman they have just made love to.' A man considers his penis to be an organ of power and appropriation. Defining sexual males as the Daddy and the rapist at the same time, Reynaud goes on to say that 'the man creates a reign of fear to enable him to protect. Once a woman has been exclusively appropriated, the man guarantees protection, and tries to treat "his" woman as a child. A woman is not supposed to be capable of looking after herself.'

When a man wants to use a woman for sexual purposes, he has little concern for her feelings, declares Reynaud, and once the conquest is over the relationship often bores him. We can certainly see this in operation in male fantasy fiction. James Bond changes his sexual partner with every new adventure, and no lasting relationship is ever established.

The sexual side of an average marriage, according to Reynaud, eventually comes down to a permanent 'land-lord's due' that the husband exacts twice a week, once a week, every night, or whenever.

With men, although not with women, sex and violence are inextricably linked together. Women would like sex to be gentle, but men want to be aggressive. A novel or film that features sex will more often than not include violence as well. So often does this happen that the term 'sex-and-violence' had come to characterize a whole genre of what passes for entertainment. We do not speak in the same breath of 'sex and vegetarianism' or 'sex and prayer', because the two concepts are miles apart. But sex and violence are linked in a very intimate way. In order to be sexual at all, men have to exert a degree of violence and force – otherwise the penis will not penetrate the vagina. This is by no means always realized or understood, but it is a fact.

Rape is so widespread, so universal, that we often fail to recognize it as such. It happens, however, at times, in every single heterosexual relationship. In an article on the subject in *The Guardian*, Jonathan Rutherford pointed out that 'while men continue with their present behaviour, there can be no real peace . . .' Rape, he continued, is essentially about male sexuality, and the values it has produced.

'Our sexual practice,' he wrote, 'is overwhelmingly goal-oriented towards penetration and orgasm . . . Men are encouraged to revel in the myth that a predatory phallocentric sexuality, divorced from any moral or emotional obligations, is what nature intended.'

Feminists will of course be familiar with these arguments, but here they are being put forward by men. It seems that even men now realize that the obsession with sexual gratification and sexual pleasure has gone too far, and has not achieved what was expected or hoped.

So, are men more sexually inclined than women? The answer has to be yes: in our present society they are. And look where all this insistence on the importance of expressing ourselves sexually has led us: men are not noticeably happier, more content or at peace with themselves and the world than in the days when they were expected to try to curb their sexual appetites. The sexual revolution – for men, at least – started off with some good intentions. It was thought, in the dark, far-off days of the 1950s, that it was wrong to repress sexual feelings, and that by denying sexuality in ourselves we were cutting ourselves off from a vital life force. As some kind of sexual fusion is essential in the majority of species for reproduction, it seems logical to believe that sexuality – however we decide to define it – is in itself somehow creative, magical, imbued with mystical meaning.

Jenny James, who runs a commune in a remote part of Ireland and who sees herself as a therapist freeing men from their pent-up repressions, fear of and guilt about sex, said in a magazine interview recently: 'All the major religions in the world want us to repress our sexuality and in exchange hand us some vague hope of a life hereafter.' Jenny is convinced that repressing bad feelings, such as a fear of sex, anger or guilt, leads to our becoming blocked as people: it is wrong, she believes, to stifle emotions.

Many American psychologists of the 'sixties and early 'seventies propounded a similar idea, that repressing sexual feelings leads to many illnesses and psychiatric problems. The way to inner reality and peace, they believed, was to express oneself sexually, as gloriously and uninhibitedly as possible.

These were all good and worthy aims, no doubt, but they have not led to any diminution of fear or guilt. Nor have they improved human relationships. What has happened in fact during the last twenty years is a steady increase in anger, violence and the number of sexual atrocities being committed. These will continue to increase if the sexual urge, with its highly addictive and uncontainable potential, is allowed to get even further out of hand. We now have the idea that everybody, whatever their sexual persuasion, has the 'right' to fulfil themselves in a sexual manner, and that we should not interfere with this right as long as it takes place between 'consenting adults' and there is no coercion or force.

But by putting so much energy into the sexual act, by concentrating so much creativity into the genital area, we have actually succeeded in adding to the sum of the world's confusion and unhappiness.

The incidence of rape and child sexual abuse is greatly on the increase. According to a MORI poll, one in 10 adults have been sexually assaulted as children, and more than a million children in Britain can now expect to be sexually assaulted at some point in their childhood. Men rape because they cannot seem to get enough sex. The women they meet in real life are never as willing and eager as those in their fantasies, but deep down, of course, they 'want it', so a little bit of force won't matter, thinks the rapist. But rape, as so many experts on the subject have indicated, has very little to do with sexual desire and everything to do with exerting power and control and subduing the woman. We shall never start to reduce the rape figures, which are now beginning to horrify men as well as women, until men can start to see the attractions and benefits of a more celibate attitude to life.

When a man's whole being is consumed with thoughts about sex, he becomes constantly anxious and depressed. The sense of satisfaction, as with any other addiction, is quickly lost as there is no way the sex urge can ever become satisfied. There is some evidence to suggest that before men engage in sex at all, it hardly preys on their minds; but once sexuality has become important they can hardly think of anything else. In India, where arranged marriages are still the norm, extra-marital sex is relatively rare, and men as well as women are supposed to be virgins on marriage. A surprising amount of men do remain virgins until their wedding night, as there may be little opportunity for premarital sexual liaisons. Yet as soon as a man marries, whether at age 13 or age 45, he starts to feel he cannot do without sex. Every time sexual intercourse happens, the habit becomes further ingrained, and it may seem positively painful to go without it for more than a week or so. Once men stop indulging in sex so often, the urge does not become ever more desperate, but gradually starts to recede. It is not that it is repressed or sublimated; it simply goes away.

In order for a non-religious man to appreciate the positive side of celibacy he must be convinced that there is something better in the offing, that his life will actually be improved as a result. When men become celibate not through choice, perhaps because they are simply unable to find a sexual partner, they often have a terrible feeling of deprivation. When this is the case, the likelihood that a man will commit a sex crime, or try to force a woman into sex, is increased. The answer is, however, not to try to satisfy that sexual desire, which grows ever stronger the more it is indulged, but to enable men to see that sex is a phantom, a chimera that promises much but delivers little.

Primarily, a decision to embrace celibacy, at least for a time, allows a man to direct important energies elsewhere. Sex is ultimately time-wasting and purposeless. By keeping his brain between his legs, a man is missing much of what he could be experiencing. Through sex, a man can forget himself temporarily, but he will never learn what he is really capable of.

For heterosexual men, at least, unless they are paying a prostitute, a sexual relationship implies some kind of commitment to the other person. Any man involved with a sexual partner will know how much anxiety the sex act causes, as a constant occurrence. Will she say yes, will tonight be the night, or will he be spurned yet again? Will she agree to anal or oral sex to ring the changes? The man who lives for sex, or who sees it as central and necessary to his life, will inevitably have to put up with a large amount of rejection and failure. In addition, he will probably worry whether he will be a good lover or not, whether his present partner will compare him unfavourably with other men, whether she will be bored out of her mind, passive, unaroused, scream in pain, or otherwise give a negative response. After a time with the same partner, the man will begin to notice that she is by degrees becoming ever less interested in sex and finds reasons to push him away and say, 'Not tonight'. Many men feel that such snubs and constant rejection are worth it for the occasions of successful intercourse, but of course the man then becomes horribly dependent on a woman who may be either sublimely indifferent or actively hostile to his sexual advances.

That energetic, frequent sex does not result in any strengthening of bonds can be seen from the divorce figures. The partners, having been fooled into believing that sex is important, find that they gradually grow to hate each other. One reason for that is that, in a modern marriage, there is no privacy for either partner. The couple share a bed, and the woman is supposed to be always available.

The great majority of marriages break up because one or both partners is having an affair with somebody else. If sex were as normal and natural and healthy as some insist, why should extra-marital sex be considered cheating, and qualify as grounds for divorce?

Men use sex primarily as a means of domination. Yet, paradoxically, it is plain that such attempts to dominate do not put the man in control, nor do they ensure lasting happiness or an equal relationship. A man may believe he has married a compliant, sexy, feminine girl, but all too soon this once-passive woman will become uppity and start to assert herself. She will wheedle, she will deny him sex, or show him up in public. It is observable that most married couples who are having a sexual relationship find every opportunity to do the other down, to denigrate their spouse. I would go so far as to say that *any* long-term sexual relationship between a man and a woman creates a measure of ill feeling and hostility. Eventually, unless a relationship can progress beyond the sexual, the couple in question will cease to respect, and ultimately despise, each other.

When a woman has a sexual relationship with a man she feels entitled to make demands on him, which he may not want. There is mutual dependence, which serves only to feed the other's weakness. Furthermore, it is not as if a man can relate to just one woman – 'his' woman – in a sexual way, and see other women as non-sexual. If he has become used to regarding women as sexual creatures, he will judge every woman in this light. The writer Graham Greene says in one of his novels that there are few things more dismal than dining with an unattractive female.

Would a heterosexual male say the same thing about dining out with another man?

The sex urge does not free men, nor does it allow pent-up frustrations to escape from the system. Rather, it makes them grow so that in time yet more frustration and more anger build up. The more powerful a man's sex drive becomes, the less able he is to relate to women as proper human beings. When dependent on women for sex, the man eventually comes to hate them, for he perceives them as being capricious – either giving or withholding sexual contact according to whim.

The phrase 'wine, women and song' is so common we hardly think about what it conveys. But of course, what it does mean is that for a man, a woman may be seen as one of the more indulgent pleasures of life: a plaything, a novelty, a toy, an addiction. Very often in the more lurid sex cases reported in the newspapers, we learn that some frightful middle-aged man has 'provided' girls for some vice ring or other. Women can still be treated as a commodity, something dispensable, relatively unimportant, to be discarded when no longer useful or sexually pleasing.

Men traditionally want to control women because, from the dawn of history, they have been afraid of them. Women have been seen as creatures who exist to lure, ensnare and lead men into temptation. For sexually-inclined men, women are seen as half-human creatures on the edge of life, peripheral people who do not really matter and can be forgotten when the real (men's) business takes place. When men regard all women as sexual, they will try to reduce them to sex objects. In a recent article in *You* magazine by Anthony Burgess this attitude was shown at its most ridiculous when he described the prime minister, Mrs Thatcher, as exerting a strongly sexual aura along with her power: 'It is the drive that counts, and drive always has a lot of sex in it,' pontificated Mr Burgess. Only in an age saturated with sex could a man say this about a 60-year-old woman, one who has never played on any aspect of female sexuality to win herself political power. In our shameful misuse of the word 'sexual' we have come to equate it with a kind of power, charisma and attractiveness, reducing everything to the genital.

When somebody describes a world leader such as Mrs Thatcher as 'sexual', it implies an attempt to reduce her standing as an individual, to dismiss her impact upon people as a stirring of the loins. It is only when men can forget about women being sexual, and relate to them in ways other than physical, that they can begin to regard them as human beings and feel genuine respect for them.

Men have for so long regarded women as sexual creatures that, when homosexuality 'came out', it was inevitable that men should start regarding each other as bodies. Many male homosexuals have a huge variety of partners, but in very few cases do they ever establish, or even want to establish, a close emotional relationship. There are cases, of course, of homosexuals who love each other devotedly and are as faithful as some heterosexual couples, but they are very much in the minority.

In his biography of the homosexual playwright Joe Orton, the writer John Lahr (son of the actor Bert Lahr, who played the cowardly lion in the film *The Wizard of Oz*) describes how Orton and other gays would frequent men's lavatories and, by an elaborate ritual of mutually understood signals, discover who else in the lavatory was an active homosexual. Most of these liaisons took place without the two protagonists ever seeing each other's faces. Nor did either want to know who the other was: they were just bodies to each other. Where *both* participants seek this dismal kind of coupling, perhaps it does not do to be too censorious. But in most heterosexual relationships, the woman will not want to be so used, not least because she cannot use her partner in the same way. The point about the zipless homosexual encounter is that both parties can be either active or passive, as the mood and opportunity suit them.

Although men may believe they want to have emotion-free sexual encounters with women, they in fact have very little respect for those women who make a business out of selling sex. Such women are usually referred to as common prostitutes, harlots or whores – all pejorative terms. Women who sell their bodies for sex are usually regarded as the very lowest type of human being, the most depraved in society. Yet it is men who persist in regarding all women as sex objects. Paradoxically, a man's respect for a woman increases when he understands she is not available sexually, either to him or to any other man. Most men are distinctly in awe of nuns, for instance, and say they are unable to relate to them 'as women' – in other words, as sexual objects. There is, even to the most sex-befuddled male, a perception that this asexual-by-choice woman has some extra dimension, some extra power. Of course, the power of the Virgin Mary, for Catholics, lies in her perpetual virginity. She has never been defiled by a mere human male, only impregnated by the Holy Ghost, who does not possess a body.

Though men go to women for sex, they still regard those women who spread their sexual favours around freely as cheap tarts or nymphomaniacs. There is confusion everywhere because we have come to feel that, first and foremost, we should relate to people of the opposite gender in a sexual way; we simply do not know how else to see them. It is a desperately selfish and self-centred way to try to relate to other people. When a man treats a woman as just a sexual object he misses a lot of what she has to offer, her uniqueness as a human being.

Men cannot be truly liberated until they learn to see women as non-sexual. Of course it is by no means always the man's fault that he sees women mainly in sexual terms. Women, too, have the idea that they are worth more as human beings if they are sexually attractive, and have played on this throughout the ages. In the 'eighties the idea of women as sex objects is stronger than ever, so that we now have the topsy-turvy situation where young girls who pose nude in magazines and newspapers can become millionaires practically overnight. Some earn more than the prime minister by this means, and feel extremely proud that they can earn money just by being women.

In an article in *The Sunday Times* in January 1986, Helen Mason drew attention to the present day pin-up phenomenon, stressing how very dangerous it all was. In the old days, she said, pin-ups were remote beauties, as unattainable as a moonbeam. The gap, Ms Mason said, 'between fantasy figures and actual females was wide and fixed'. Now, however, the pin-up may be, and often is, the girl next door. These girls seem to be highly available. 'How unfair it may seem to the average male,' wrote Helen Mason, 'his appetite whetted by a flick through the magazines, to walk down a street ignored by available girls. They are products, explicitly displayed, which he is being denied.'

Ms Mason concluded thus: 'Feminists tear up pin-ups because they are insulting to women. I think they are more than that. I think they are dangerous. And I wish the girls who pose for them thought so too.'

And there we have it. If sex was, as Dr Alex Comfort and countless others have tried to persuade us, the natural expression of a deep-seated need, there would be no pornography, no rape, no sexual abuse of women by men. *Why* are there so many rape cases? *Why* is there so much sexual abuse of pre-adolescent children? If women are as eager as men for sex, why are there still prostitutes making a good living? If sex is normal and healthy, why is there so much sexual harassment at work?

Why do so many men have to resort to threats and violence to persuade women to have sex with them? Why does sex lead to violence of all kinds, and not just specifically sexual violence?

It is because we have become obsessed with sex and because so many sexual images are now presented to men that they feel deprived if they are not getting all they imagine they should have. The present situation will never improve; indeed, it can only worsen while we continue to place such importance on the physical act of sex. Men and women have to learn that it is celibacy, rather than sex, which can bring about real power, because celibacy removes one's dependency for happiness upon another person's body.

It might seem that I am crying in the wilderness, that I am a lone voice advising something that will only ever have minority interest for the great proportion of men. But no. There are rumblings of discontent with the present situation from men themselves. The once-great Playboy empire, started by Hugh Hefner in an attempt to make sex more fun and less serious, more recreational and less guilt-ridden, is now fading fast, and Hefner himself lives the life of a recluse. The present generation of men do not want to be served meals by vapid, sexy-looking Bunny girls, as they have learned from their father's generation that the 'Look – don't touch' provocation they offer causes only misery and discontent. And a survey in January 1985 by Mike Royko, an American columnist, revealed that for the average American male golf and fishing could be more satisfying and enjoyable than sex.

One golfer who was questioned observed: 'At least my buddies on the links are amused by my inadequacies, inabilities and ineptness. They are laughing *with* me, not *at* me.'

Another golfer enthused: 'Five hours on 150 acres of perfectly manicured beauty, breathing fresh air, experiencing the excitement of pars and birdies with my best friends, compared to five minutes of love-making with 150 pounds of not-so-manicured woman who constantly complains about my lack of income and lack of understanding: it is no contest.'

A fisherman said: 'Let's face it, sex can't compete with the feeling one gets in landing a seven-pound bass.'

Humorous and tongue-in-cheek these quotes may be, but like all humour they convey a deep truth. Men really know that they will never gain peace and happiness through sex, but they just feel they cannot do without it. Sex has an almighty hold on them, and they are reluctant, indeed fearful, to let it go.

Women also have to realize that 'real' men are not like those described in the typical Harold Robbins novel, capable of producing gigantic hard-ons at the same time as running successful world empires; they are those who have learned to treat women as equal human beings, equally precious, equally important, equally responsible and equally worthy of respect. But until women themselves can relinquish the habit of relating to men in a sexual way, this will never happen.

Men who have been addicted to gambling, nicotine, alcohol or drugs always speak of the wonderful freedom they experience after they have managed to kick the habit. They love the feeling of no longer being dependent on something that may not always be available. The same can happen for a man who comes to decide that physical sex need not be so central to his life. He can then become friends with women, the other half of the human race, instead of seeing them either as temptresses, or sexually frigid.

CHAPTER 7

Celibacy and marriage

Seven of us were sitting round a dinner table. There were six women and one man. All except one were either married or living with long-term partners. When I mentioned that I was researching a book on the subject of celibacy, everybody immediately stopped their conversations and became interested. 'What about marriage?' one of the guests asked. 'Yes, I think celibacy can be a good idea in marriage too,' I replied.

Instead of the expected stares of disbelief and amazement, there were instant nods of agreement. One by one the married women sitting round the dinner table confessed that they did not like sex very much. They hesitated to admit it, thinking there must be something wrong with them. Alison, a well-known TV reporter, aged 29 and married for two years, said that she could not understand it at all. She fully expected to enjoy sex, but simply did not. Her husband did, unfortunately. Should she continue to fake it, she wondered? After all, she has been married such a very short time.

Laura, a very glamorous 39-year-old who runs a highly successful public relations firm, was married to a younger man. It was her second marriage. She said wryly: 'I've been tired every single night for the past five years including Sundays. *Why* don't I like sex? Should I?'

Margaret, who was also married for the second time, had been a model and now worked as a secretary. Aged 42, still with model-girl looks and figure, she said that at her age she felt she had had enough, and was completely past being even remotely interested in sex. Her husband, however, was still keen and she was worried that he would feel rejected if she kept refusing him.

Anthea, aged 49, and divorced, had been living with the same man in a steady partnership for 10 years. She admitted she had no interest in sex whatever, but was disturbed by books telling her that women approaching 50 could be even more passionate in sexual matters than those 20 or 30 years younger.

Helen, the only single woman at the party, sat listening to all these confessions with interest and growing incredulity. In the end she volunteered the information that she felt so thankful she did not have a permanent partner. Aged 38, she is a solicitor in a large London practice.

All of these women were modern, 'liberated' and earning their own livings in successful careers. According to current popular mythology, they were all supposed to like and be eager for sex. They themselves expected to like it and could not understand why they did not. All thought there must be some dysfunction, which could perhaps be righted by therapy or marriage guidance. One of the women, Alison, had even considered going to a sex-therapy clinic, because she was already worried for the future of her marriage. Though all these women were highly intelligent, and successful, all confessed they felt they had to pretend to enjoy sex, otherwise their male partners would feel hurt and rejected. And that, they felt, would never do.

What of the one man present, meanwhile? He was married – though not to any of the women at this particular gathering – and listened intently to what was being said. At last he agreed that his own wife, also a career woman, was far less keen on sex than he was and he felt that the pill may have been responsible for her 'loss of libido'.

I suspect that these women sitting round the dinner table were not alone in their attitude towards sex in marriage. Whenever, over the months of researching and writing this book, I talked about it to female friends I met with much the same reaction.

Frequent comments have been: 'I could give up sex tomorrow and never miss it' and, 'At 35, I feel I've had absolutely enough, but my husband is still keen.' A few married women I spoke to voiced the fear that if they did not keep their husbands satisfied with sex, the said husbands might go off in search of more willing women.

It was very noticeable that those women who were most vociferously anti-sex were those who had careers of their own. Housewives and women who were financially dependent on men were much more fearful and timid about admitting that they did not like sex all that much.

Of course, in our own society – and probably in most societies since the beginning of time – sex and marriage are linked together. In fact, a marriage without sex is not considered a marriage at all, and can be annulled on the grounds of non-consummation. In Victorian days, women tended to feel that sex was the price they had to pay for marriage, and men were as convinced that marriage was the price they had to pay for sex. Before easy contraception made women available all the time, whether or not they were married, men usually had to buy 'extra' sex from prostitutes or mistresses. In the main, however, sex was difficult for a man unless he was married.

It was commonly supposed, in those far-off days, that the wife would not enjoy sex all that much, nor was she expected to. Actual enjoyment of the sexual act was only for ladies of easy virtue, as they were termed. But though respectable wives may not have been enthusiastic about sex, it was enshrined in the marital convention that they would have to submit to their husbands on occasion.

In former times, throughout Western society, marriage was virtually the only means of economic survival for a woman. The question of whether she would enjoy sex, when she had virtually no choice but to marry, simply did not arise, nor did it matter all that much. Sex was considered part of her sacred duty once she was married, so she simply had to put up with it. Then gradually we – that is, women – started to make a virtue out of what had been a necessity. In 1918 Marie Stopes published her famous (and at the time notorious) *Married Love*, in which she stated that thousands of married women all over the country were becoming ill with nervous complaints, all because they were left unsatisfied by sex. Women, she explained in her inimitable flowery language, were sexual beings who were perfectly capable of responding sexually, but in most cases they did not know how to turn what many considered a sordid duty into a pleasurable experience. Marie Stopes' *Married Love*, which was probably the first explicit sex manual aimed at the general market, told women not just to lie back and think of England, but to become active and joyful participants in the sexual act.

Soon after she set herself up as a marriage guidance counsellor and birth control educator, Marie Stopes came to learn that very few marriages were at all happy. The 'profound disappointment' which set in sooner or later she put down to misunderstandings about sex. If only men and women could appreciate the true nature of sexuality and learn to enjoy each other's bodies, Dr Stopes declared, marriages would become far happier and more joyful.

Over the years, we have taken Marie Stopes' advice more and more to heart – and to bed. But have marriages become noticeably any happier now that both partners are likely to be sexually experienced before the wedding day? Very few brides today may be called 'blushing' and virtually none are now virgins when they walk up the aisle in white; yet, all too demonstrably, sexual experience and know-how has not put one jot of extra enjoyment into the married state. There are far more divorces than ever before and in America, where there are far more 'how-to' sex manuals on sale even than in the UK, divorce has become the norm rather than the exception.

Sex is all too clearly *not* a magic glue that binds partners together in mystic, transcendental unions for ever and ever. In the old days, when married couples probably had far less sex than they do today, most marriages lasted. Of course there are other reasons to explain why this should be – divorce was far more difficult anyway, and most ex-wives would have had no means whatever of supporting themselves financially. In the main, therefore, couples stayed together for better or worse. But the less frequent sex was very likely a factor as well.

Yet even though all the evidence tells us that sex does not keep couples together, we persist in believing, or wanting to believe, that it does. Every year, ever more sex advice books are published, telling us how we can have wonderful orgasms with a chosen partner. One recent such volume, *The Complete Book of Sexual Fulfilment*, written by two doctors, attempts to perpetuate this myth. On the cover of the book is the usual illustration, in soft focus, of a couple in sexual bliss. Both are naked. He has dark curly hair and a sexually satisfied expression;

she has long blonde hair and an artfully posed tender look. Inside the cover, the blurb tells us: 'Human beings are neither designed nor intended to be solitary animals. We dream of our need to find love and companionship, and a complete fulfilling sexual relationship is part of that ideal.'

Oh, if only, if only! If only there were a direct connection between sexual bliss and lasting marital happiness! If only this were the case, how easy things would be. Unfortunately, life's not like that.

My own belief is that there is not necessarily any connection between sexual fulfilment (as if such a thing could ever be) and marital happiness. Furthermore, I believe that celibate marriages – or marriages in which periods of celibacy are a positive choice for both partners – have the chance of being *more* happy, *more* long-lasting and rewarding than unions in which sex has become a central activity. Such marriages cannot be happy for long, because physical sex is simply incapable of delivering long-term contentment, or enjoyment of the other person as a person. Where sex is considered an important, or essential, part of a marriage, inevitably each partner comes to be judged, at least to some extent, on physical attributes, on the shape and size of his or her body. I have known women who started to hate their husbands when they went bald or developed a paunch. Similarly, all too many husbands are apt to 'trade in' the original wife when she gets middle-aged, or grey-haired, in favour of a younger model. This is very common where the husband has become successful in the outside world and the wife has not.

It is my conviction that the more important an element sex is considered in the marriage the less likely the marriage is either to last or to be happy.

Of course, I have not always thought this. When I first married, in 1965, both my husband and I viewed sex as some kind of ultimate experience. Together we would be able to achieve never-before-dreamt-of heights of bodily bliss, we thought. And for a time that was possible. While the relationship was being established, while we were still excited by and getting to know each other, sex did indeed play an important part. We then viewed married couples who slept in single beds, or had separate rooms, as lacking in life, vigour and vitality. To us, such people seemed dead, dreary, beyond redemption. Then gradually, almost imperceptibly, our pleasure in each other's bodies began to fade. One of us would be 'too tired' or 'lacking in libido' – one of the commonest complaints, I understand, that people now take to their doctors.

When we noticed this happening, we went almost frantic with worry. What was up? Why were we not experiencing the same pleasure any more? We still liked each other, had no plans to divorce, and neither of us was having affairs with other people.

At first my husband wondered if the pill could be at fault for this continued 'loss of libido'. As a medical journalist on a national newspaper, he followed closely all the medical research on oral contraceptives, and had heard that the pill could cause lack of interest in sex. I too felt this might be the case, yet at the time was reluctant to relinquish the pill which gave such foolproof contraception.

What we did not see for many years, in common with a large number of other couples, is that our relationship over the years had to change. We could not forever be a honeymoon couple. Indeed, we would not want to be, as that would imply we were stuck in some post-adolescent phase. We also did not see, at the time, that it was both *natural* and *inevitable* that after a while we would become less interested in sex, at least with each other. Every marriage survey that has ever been conducted shows the same finding: that frequency of sexual intercourse declines gradually with every successive year of marriage. Instead of accepting this as the norm, that married couples are naturally going to lose interest in each other's bodies as the years go by, sex therapists insist that we must try to bring the 'romance' back into the relationship. So, as real interest declines, we are urged to substitute this with an artificial kind of behaviour, such as wearing 'sexy' underwear, having dinner by candlelight and taking 'second honeymoon'-type holidays. All these devices, plus other more intimate marital aids of the sort sold in sex shops, have the cumulative effect of making married couples even more miserable and dejected, more full of guilt than they were before. For try as we might, there is no way that the earth is going to move any more, and we might as well accept it. We should at the same time accept that after the sex interest fades a new, maturer phase of the relationship can be brought into being. This is a relationship that does not depend for its continuance and happiness in finding and manipulating erogenous zones, or in seeking ever more exotic means of sexual gratification from each other.

Most doctors would tell you that in their own experience about 60 per cent of their married patients have some kind of sex-related marital problem. By this they either mean something technical, such as premature ejaculation or impotence, or something emotional, such as one or other partner's gaining no positive pleasure from the sexual act. What is wrong with us, doctor? the anxious couple will ask, and the doctor – who usually knows nothing whatever of the dynamics of that particular couple's relationship – will suggest hormone treatment, sexy videos or sex therapy, or will describe specific techniques that the couple may not previously have known about. In fact, all of these will be doomed to failure. The couple will never again achieve sexual satisfaction with each other. They cannot, because as they diligently try ever more complicated methods of pleasing each other sexually they will inevitably end up bored and frustrated. So their disappointment and dissatisfaction with each other will increase. They will start to blame each other and have quarrels, and yet more anxiety and tension will result.

Once a couple becomes bored with each other sexually, there is no way of bringing sexual excitement back; so why should they not accept it gracefully, acknowledge that that side of the marriage is over and see it as a blessed release rather than as an unfortunate and unnatural occurrence?

This is what, eventually, I did in my own marriage. In the end, we gave up the pretence that sexual excitement could somehow be brought back and decided to live celibately. We moved into separate rooms, and the result for both of us has been absolute bliss. Our sex life did not end, as it does for so many couples, in acrimony, but by common consent. At first, the celibacy was intended only for a time, to give ourselves a rest from each other, and from sexual demands and expectations. But we found we much preferred the new arrangement, and it has worked to bring us closer together, not drive us further apart. Instead of being long-bored marital partners trying vainly to please each other in bed, we have now become equal friends and companions, independently existing, yet still with a close bond.

For a time, we felt rather ashamed of what we had done, and felt we had to pretend that we still had what is usually regarded as a normal marriage. Now, we do not mind advertising the fact of our celibacy because we have discovered that a non-sexual marriage works, as a sexual one did previously. After all, neither of us has any further interest in reproducing, as our family was completed long ago, so sex was ultimately sterile anyway.

In the beginning, most people looked at us oddly and hinted that with such a peculiar arrangement, the marriage would be sure to fall apart before very long. Without the glue, or Sellotape, what could hold us together? Neither of us, in the five years that have elapsed since we decided to become celibate in our marriage, has had affairs with other people, or looked for them. Physical sex has simply ceased to be an important aspect of our lives, and we have developed other interests which we find infinitely more worthwhile. We came to realize in our own marriage that by trying to remain in a sexual mode we were actually not allowing the relationship to grow, but were trying to recapture what had been an immature partnership.

In other words, we have grown up, in both our relationship to each other and the way we view ourselves. As a child, I imagined there could be no greater delight on earth or in heaven than to run a sweetshop. As a child I thought funfairs were truly magic, and could hardly contain my excitement when the annual fair visited the small town where I lived. Now that I am grown up, I cannot imagine anything more boring than running a sweetshop, and dodgems and roundabouts no longer hold an attraction either. I have grown out of the thrill I once experienced, and I am not sorry to say goodbye to it.

As a teenager, I was knowledgeable about pop music and enjoyed listening to it. I no longer do. Most adults would have no difficulty in agreeing with me so far, for most would have experienced similar feelings.

But in the matter of sex, we cannot seem to understand that physical sex cannot and should not be as important for a person of 40 as it is to somebody of 20.

As by far the greatest majority of people are married, it is time to ask: just *why* is sex considered such a vital ingredient of marriage? Why has the idea persisted that married couples have a duty to try to please each other sexually, or that, indeed, any person has a 'right' to expect some kind of sexual fulfilment to be provided by another person?

One obvious answer to this is that we all have sexual organs, and that sex is the supreme act of creation. Life is not possible without it, or was not until recently, when technology separated sex from the creation of a new life. But even with technology, somehow an egg and a sperm have to meet and become fused with each other. It is also true that ecstasy and bliss are possible through sexual acts.

In that we all possess sex organs, we can be considered sexual beings. The marriage service in the Anglican prayer book also states specifically that marriage was ordained for the procreation of children. So in that sense, people who marry each other have a duty, if they are Christians, to try to reproduce and ensure the establishment of the next generation.

As a social and cohesive insitution, marriage does make sense. From a purely biological point of view it also makes sense that the act of sex can give pleasure. After all, it is better for children to be brought up in an atmosphere in which the parents are fond of each other. What is wrong is that we have now given sex a psychic importance in our lives and a central place in marriage. It is wrong because it almost guarantees that couples will, in time, come to hate each other.

How so? Surely physical sex is meant to be an expression of love between two people? Well – who said so? Sex is just an act, and may, as we have seen, be pleasurable or hateful depending on circumstances. When people are first in love they naturally want to fuse their bodies together and become, as the marriage service says, 'one flesh'. But this does not last and in time they yearn to become separate people again. Yet they have vowed, one way or another, to 'worship' each other's bodies and they keep trying to fuse again. Having cemented the relationship, why go on trying to do so? When you have built a wall, you do not keep adding cement to the bricks: there is no need.

The same goes for a marriage relationship. Either it has bonded together in the early stages or it has not, and no super-glue sex will work if the couples do not basically want to be as one. Also, no amount of glue will ever mend a relationship that has finally broken up.

Couples who continue to have sex in time come to hate each other because sooner or later the bed will turn into a battleground. One wants it, the other does not. One makes advances, which the other rejects, saying wearily: 'Not tonight.'

Also, continuing sex is far more likely than celibacy to lead to extra-marital affairs, with all the jealousy, double-dealing, deceit and added stress which such an affair always entails. This is how it happens. The average couple find physical delight in each other's bodies for a few years. They believe, as I did myself, that a marriage without regular sex is an empty relationship, one which has no substance. After a time, however, the delight fades. As they have been taught that sex is important, nay vital, to their lives, they try to recapture that delight. They realize this is impossible with each other but remain convinced that sexual fulfilment is important. They may well start to look outside the marriage for the delight that they had within marriage all those years ago. This is usually easily found; it is not difficult to discover new bliss with a new partner. They are then confronted with the agonizing contrast between the bliss experienced in the lover's arms and the indifference of the marriage partner. This serves to widen even further the rift between the couple. Before long, they may start to accuse each other: the husband may call his wife 'frigid', recalling how responsive his mistress is, and the wife may say that her husband has always been a useless lover anyway.

If she too has embarked on an affair, she will be contrasting the lack of sensation with her husband with the transports of delight she experiences with her lover.

Such scenes are all too common between couples, and most, if not all, married people will find the scenario familiar. Sex serves to drive couples apart rather than keep them together, because basically they will be looking to the other person to satisfy frustration. Both husband and wife nowadays imagine they have a right to sexual satisfaction, and may feel extremely fed up with the other if this is not forthcoming.

There can in reality be no equality when a marriage continues to be sexual. Nor can there be a free, open and truly loving partnership. As sex is basically an addiction, the more it is fed the more it will be wanted and expected. In so-called modern marriages, it is assumed that the wife will at all times be freely available for her husband. During the 1970s, the myth of the superwoman gave us to believe that a wife, ideally, had to be at the same time successful career woman, superb cook and wonderful lover. That was, in the words of the era, 'having it all'. Very many women can cope quite easily with being the first two, but the last requirement confounds them. Why should women have to be such wonderful lovers? What enhancement will it bring to their lives, or indeed those of their husbands, whose addiction to sex will be kept alive all the time?

There can never be equality between the sexes, especially in marriage, where the wife continues to be seen as the provider of sex. Some women have alleged that they are the instigators of sex, and that they married their husbands for their gorgeous bodies or some other physical attribute. But that is just another example of how some women – wanting to appear liberated and up to date – have taken over the male attitude and adopted the male method of trying to exert power and control, rather than trying to establish a friendship between equals.

A man traditionally knows that to have sexual intercourse with a woman means to exert power over her, and no amount of sexual aggression by women will alter this fundamental fact. Anatomical construction alone demonstrates that this must be the case. In order to have sexual intercourse at all a man must have an erection and penetrate. In other words, he must be active. The woman may be either active or passive, but her own reaction will not make much difference. Sex can still happen, however passive the woman may be; if the man is passive, it simply cannot take place.

In elevating sex into a religion, we have dismissed as unnaturally repressive what ancient religions had to say on the subject of sex and marriage. In the Bible, we read that there are certain times when a man may not have intercourse with his wife: during and for seven days after menstruation, and during and just after pregnancy. In fact, these are all the times when the woman would be infertile. Sex was supposed to be procreational rather than recreational. The Catholic Church took over this Judaic idea, and in forbidding all forms of birth control endorsed the belief that sex was primarily to be used for reproduction, not for relieving frustrations and anxieties. The basic idea behind the Catholic ban on birth control was not to populate the world with Catholics but to restrict sex to reproduction. In our more 'enlightened' times we have laughed at these restrictions, regarding them as the edicts of celibate, dried-up old men who have never themselves experienced an atom of sexual desire.

We have come to see religiously imposed sexual restrictions in marriage as deadening, repressive and inimical to the life force, forgetting that these rules were originally made for the benefit of humanity. Ancient wisdom acknowledged that sex could be a dangerous force which, unrestricted, could grow into an insatiable monster. The current insistence that sex must take place at all times within marriage means that those who perceive they are not getting 'enough' may go out to commit acts of outrage, such as child sexual abuse, rape, or other crimes of sex or violence. Indeed, many present-day sex manuals go so far as to say that, if more wives catered to their husband's sexual needs, far fewer sex crimes would be committed, as fewer men would have to go out and try to satisfy themselves in antisocial ways. Here, they are totally wrong. The more sex people have, the more they want – not the other way round.

Germaine Greer recognized the truth of this in her book

Sex and Destiny. Once her views became known, she was denigrated as being 46 years old and frumpy by national newspapers, which tried to dismiss what she had said. Yet we inwardly know that when she claims that modern women are supposed to be perpetual geisha girls for their husbands, she is right.

She writes: 'Having fun means recreational sex; recreational sex means no fear of pregnancy, a wife who is always available, and who is content with orgasms in place of land, family and children – orgasms and consumer durables.'

In describing sex as the new 'opiate of the people', she continues:

The new opiate of the people, like all religions, has its ritual observance. The discipline imposed is the discipline of the orgasm, not just any orgasm, but the perfect orgasm, regular, spontaneous, potent and reliable. The blessed are laid-back, into their bodies, in touch with themselves. They shrink from no penetration, they feel no invasion of self, they fear nothing and regret nothing, they defy jealousy. The regular recurrence of orgasms provides the proof that they are in a state of grace. To object that orgasm is itself inadequate to this high purpose is to expose oneself as orgiastically impotent, for sex religion, like all others, relies on self-fulfilling prophecies. To the faithful, who believe that orgasms will release tension, make all potentialities accessible, dissipate discontent and aggression and stabilize the ego in its right relation to the world, all these are achieved when the sacred duty is discharged. Those who rise from orgasms sad or angry, disappointed or bored, are themselves at fault. They have held something back, harboured deep scepticism: they are the self-destructive.

Modern sex religion, adds Germaine Greer, declares that sex is the most potent force in the world and its power is ineluctable.

We have elevated sex into a religion that has to be observed whatever the ages and inclinations of the partners. Even Marie Stopes, who encouraged all women to take a positive pleasure in sex, acknowledged that couples may, over the years, reduce or abandon their former sexual activity for the sake of a higher ideal.

There are subtle traps for both men and women who consider that sex is all-important in marriage. Sex keeps a couple mutually dependent on each other and makes them rely for their happiness and psychic release on the partner's body. When for any reason the usual body is not there, either could feel that it must be replaced by somebody else. As Germaine Greer points out, many men in their mid-thirties feel that if they have to endure more than two days of celibacy they will burst. One common fallacy is that sperm will build up and erupt like a volcano in time. In fact, nothing could be further from the truth; sperm does not continue to be manufactured in this way. Otherwise celibacy would be a physical impossibility, and our knowledge of physiology tells us this is not so.

When a married couple imagines that sex is important to their lives, they may blame deep personal dissatisfactions on the sexual aspect of their relationship rather than looking deeper for the cause of the trouble.

In *Sex and Destiny* Germaine Greer draws distinctions between traditional societies, commonly assumed to be sex-mad, and our own present society, which actually is sex-mad. Married couples in most traditional societies observe periods of abstinence from sex; moreover the existence of the extended family means that they are less frequently left to their own devices. Married couples nowadays expect far too much from sex, and are disappointed and bewildered when their sex lives cease to be exciting.

As there is no way of ensuring continued sexual excitement, it is far better for couples to consider other ways of relating to each other and to decide to call it a day when sex causes more problems than it solves.

On the practical level, it can be very difficult for one partner in a marriage to be the one to say, 'No more sex.' Inevitably, the other will feel rejected, hurt and anxious, for it is assumed in our society that if somebody no longer wants to have sex with you, he or she does not like you as a person any more.

One married woman, aged 35, told me how she set about ending her sexual relationship with her dearly-loved husband. Isabel, who has two children aged 10 and 6 and also runs a travel agency, had been celibate for six months when I spoke to her, and had no intention of resuming sex with her husband, or, indeed, anybody else.

'When we first married,' she said, 'I used to enjoy sex a lot and look forward to it. But after a time I came to feel that it was making me more anxious and detracting from the energies I could have given to other things.

'Although I am married with a family, I never wanted to be dependent on a man, and gradually it dawned on me that through sex I was still being dependent. I was relying on somebody else for my own happiness and satisfaction, and suddenly it seemed to me that this was wrong.

'In any marriage, it's always unlikely that sex will work perfectly. One may feel like sex when the other doesn't, and it is very rare that the desire and satisfaction are going to be equal for both partners. The level of interest is always going to be different for each person.

'When you are young and first in love, you can seem equal in your ardour. But for me, when I'd been married for a few years, I found that sex caused a lot of extra pressure. We all want an ideal sexual relationship, or think we do, and yet we can never achieve it, because it's impossible. In the end, sex becomes a habit, something you do because it has always been an integral part of the relationship.

'In the beginning, you can't get enough of each other but you soon realize that the physical sex has nothing at all to do with love. Most often, the emotions involved are extremely negative and come down to domination by the man. Really, it's always up to him how long sexual intercourse lasts, and the woman can never initiate sex, however much she may want to. In the end, it depends on the man's ability to have an erection, and if he is temporarily impotent, or suffers from premature ejaculation, there is not a lot she can do about it.

'Even though our generation was brought up to believe men and women can be equal sexually, in any marriage you find that this is not so.

'It was very difficult to say to my husband that I didn't want to have physical sex any more. For ages I put it off, but in the end I felt I had to say something, and it was a tremendous relief. I've now come to the understanding that sex is a bondage. Far from freeing couples, it makes them continue to be mutually dependent and weak.

'Since becoming celibate, I've found I can have far

better relationships with men. When I'm with a man in the course of my work, or I'm travelling with a man on business, I now know for a certainty that nothing is going to happen. When I was still seeing myself sexually, there was always liable to be a moment or two of awkwardness, especially when my business involves overnight stays in hotels.

'Now I'm not relating to men sexually, I can see them as they really are, without having to worry about whether I find them attractive. They are just human beings, whereas before, inevitably, I would see them to some degree in terms of their sexual attractiveness.

'On the whole, I don't tell people that we are celibate as I'm not sure they would understand. I feel I would get peculiar looks and comments, so for the moment we are keeping it to ourselves.

'When I first mentioned the idea of celibacy to my husband, he was very surprised and rather angry, but he was prepared to go along with it. I think he felt at first that it was only a temporary thing, but now he knows that I mean it. His attitude has since changed completely, and he is relieved as well.

'The absence of sex has made us entirely reassess our relationship. Already, it has started to be better and more mature. We have both now come to see that the sexual element prevents you from seeing the other person as he really is.

'The other point about sex is that, when it comes down to it, you are doing it to please yourself, not to give happiness to the other person. It's your own satisfaction you are thinking about, your own kick you are after. I don't think sex can bond a relationship together, because you are always being selfish, and that has little to do with real love.

'But the main thing was that I wanted to be truly independent of other people. Also, as you get older, sex becomes undignified. It's very unattractive to be lustful, especially when your body no longer has the freshness and appeal of an 18-year-old's.

'The other thing about becoming celibate is that I find I have a different, healthier and cleaner outlook on life in other respects. My personality has become more stable and I feel more that I am capable of creating my own happiness. I don't need these physical things. For me, celibacy has also meant drinking less and changing my diet to a healthier one. I don't feel I'm a victim any more.

'I am convinced, though, that as a woman my decision to become celibate was made possible by the fact that I am and always have been financially independent. So many women I know would like to forget about the sex in their lives – but they are frightened, as they fear their husbands will walk off and leave them. I would say that being financially independent was one of the main things that gave me the confidence to become celibate.

'I did have to make a unilateral decision, but my husband hasn't gone off with another woman, and I know he won't. He says it's a relief for him not to worry about sex all the time. He's very successful in his work as a senior civil servant, and admits now that sex was becoming a burden for him as well.

'I know now that sex never cements a relationship. It only ever adds problems. Sex reminds a couple of their honeymoon days and can act as an escape route but it never gives you real strength. It's a false solution to problems and in the end you have to find individual, personal strength in some other way.

'I haven't changed my dress or appearance since becoming celibate. I never dressed up for my husband anyway, so there's no difference there, but of course I have to look smart for work.

'So many women I know find that after a time all they have to offer is sex, and they worry that their husbands may be getting tired of them. I see it happening all around me. The women get dejected because they are sensing that their husbands are no longer responding sexually to them as they once did.

'A lot of people won't admit it, but most 35- to 40-year-old married couples I know have absolutely rotten sex lives and wonder why.

'So far, I have found absolutely no drawbacks to becoming celibate. I feel far more energetic and have more time for my work, but that's not the major benefit. The biggest plus is that I am far more stable in myself, as I no longer have the ups and downs and rushes of emotion that accompanied physical sex. Celibacy, I find, gives me that independent strength, and this is something I need.

'I can't imagine wanting sex again, ever. Just the thought of starting all that up, with its many implications and problems, appals me. There is no thought whatsoever that I would want to have an affair with somebody outside my marriage, either. To me, that is squalid and miserable.

'I feel now that the so-called liberation of women that took place in the 'seventies actually did the complete opposite. All it did was to put women in a worse position than they were before and make them feel there was something wrong with them if they didn't want sex all the time. The pressure to be sexual added a huge extra burden to women's lives, and also those of men.'

In a recent interview Dr Prudence Tunnadine, director of the Institute of Psychosexual Studies and author of the book *The Making of Love*, told me she could not agree with the above views. 'I don't think celibacy allows women to become stronger and more independent. In fact a good sex relationship, where it is loving and equal, actually fills you with energy and vigour.

'I don't think celibacy is to be generally recommended,' she said. 'It is a way of life for extraordinary, not ordinary, people.'

But Isabel *is* an 'ordinary woman'. Though she runs a successful business she is not, and probably never will be, a great creative genius. Her own feeling is that by practising celibacy she was able to become a much more special and individual person. Her own personality was able to be released, and given true expression, when she no longer had the burden of having to be sexual in her marriage, long after the need for sex had passed.

Isabel is convinced that many of the unhappy couples she sees around her every day could improve their relationships if they only realized that sex does not bring couples closer together, mentally or emotionally, and that intimate bodily contact has no connection, necessarily, with what wedlock should be all about – as Shakespeare said, 'a marriage of true minds'.

CHAPTER 8

Celibacy and intimacy

In our society, it has long been taken for granted that it is a good thing to experience a close, loving, intimate and lasting relationship with a member of the opposite sex. Currently, many books and articles are offering advice on how to achieve this rapturous state, and we are constantly being instructed on how to 'bring back the romance' to a relationship that may be flagging or have become tired. We are also urged to try to make ourselves once more into the young and carefree person our partner married.

We can be sure that physical sex will figure very prominently in this advice. We have been told in article after article and book after book, until we have come to believe it, that a satisfying adult relationship must necessarily include sex. If not, it cannot be a 'proper' relationship. In all this, the word 'intimacy' has somehow become almost synonymous with the word 'sex', so that when we speak of a relationship being intimate we mean one in which sexual intercourse takes place. In the old days of divorce trials, judges used to speak of 'intimacy' having occurred when adulterous lovers were accused of engaging in illicit sexual intercourse.

As the law stood until 1969, the act of sex with someone other than the marital partner constituted grounds for divorce, but if this could not be proved a divorce might not be granted. The issue in determining 'how far' the relationship had gone, how intimate it had become, was physical sex.

But, as I shall try to show in the course of this chapter, genuine intimacy between two human beings need have nothing whatever to do with sex. Nor need physical union have anything to do with intimacy. Indeed, the reverse is true. In any human interaction in which bodily sex is seen as a priority, mental and emotional intimacy are in distinct danger of becoming lost. A good love life is not at all the same thing as a good sex life. The latter is easily available to anybody, if by 'good' one means 'frequent', but the former requires special personal qualities which are quite unrelated to being technically proficient in bed.

Two extreme examples illustrate clearly how the physical sex act need have nothing whatever to do with real intimacy, friendship or regard for the other person. In one sense, a prostitute has extremely intimate contact with her clients, yet it is virtually unknown for any kind of emotional relationship to develop. It is actually far more common for a prostitute to despise her clients: the urgent male need for sex, which brings her custom and income, is seen by her as a weakness to be exploited rather than as a precursor to a loving relationship.

In a recent television programme on the subject, prostitutes explained that they never permitted any kissing or fondling during intercourse, in case any rapport should develop between themselves and the clients. The prostitutes simply did not want to get to know their clients as human beings, and most admitted that they did not like men anyway. All said that, when off duty, they certainly did not want to have sex with a boyfriend. Their attitude was that, since they spent their lives charging for sex, they were not going to let a 'loving' partner have it for free. Most said they were lesbian, or asexual, in their private lives.

Most prostitutes deeply despise their clients, whom they see as weak, fearful creatures. The fact that sex forms the exclusive basis of the interaction means that neither party has any respect whatever for the other.

The other extreme example is, of course, relationships between promiscuous homosexual men, as described on page 117. Not only do these men not know each other as people, they do not want to know each other, and they go out of their way to avoid having any kind of emotional or mental kind of relationship. Promiscuous homosexuality has led, in our times, to the plague of AIDS, and means that these men are now having to reassess their values. However, a non-involving physical relationship is what many male homosexuals prefer.

Most ordinary heterosexual relationships do not, of

course, fall into either of these two categories, but in some cases they can come very close: more men and women than ever before are now engaging in a series of loveless sexual liaisons.

In her books *Fear of Flying, How to Save Your Own Life* and *Parachutes and Kisses*, American writer Erica Jong describes the search of her heroine, Isadora Wing, for the 'zipless' encounter in which sex would take place without any preliminaries, and without any emotions being tied up in the process. In the books, Isadora views the female tendency to want to become emotionally entangled with male sexual partners as a weakness, and longs for the kind of objectivity about sex that men seem to be able to have. Needless to say, the heroine discovers that the 'zipless' encounter is practically an impossibility.

A second's thought will indicate that there is no necessary link between sex and true intimacy at all. But we hold on to the idea that sex is somehow essential to human life, sanity, and for keeping a long-term relationship alive and exciting. If you are failing to turn on, or be turned on by, your partner, so the prevailing idea goes, then why not look around for some casual, 'harmless' sex, as a way of injecting some excitement into the permanent relationship, and into your life?

But the concept that humans can do without sex, and can actually become far more intimate with each other when sexual intercourse does not take place, finds little popularity in our current view of human relationships. My own feeling is that the more sex takes place, the less likelihood there is that true intimacy will ever develop. Physical sex actually prevents you from getting to know another person as a person.

So what exactly is intimacy, and how have we come to confuse it with the sexual act? Partly, of course, it is a matter of language. The words 'intimacy' and 'love' have for so long been used as euphemisms for sex that they have become all but indistinguishable from each other in our minds. Newspaper headlines such as 'Are you in the mood for love?' and 'Love-crazy housewives', or 'Rock group's intimate encounters' let you know at once that the story following is about sex, and has nothing at all to do with love or any kind of genuine intimacy.

As language serves to enable us to express our ideas, we can be sure that semantic confusion is reflected in an ideological confusion as well. Although sexual intercourse may not in itself lead to emotional intimacy, many of us think it is actually impossible to become really close and loving unless our strong feeling is expressed physically.

The dictionary definition of 'intimate' (from the Latin *'intimus'*) is 'most inward', 'deep-seated', 'a quality of close familiarity'. Most dictionaries also list its other meaning, 'illicit sex'.

Why do we continue to assume that sex and intimacy have any link with each other, or that they have anything in common at all?

I believe we need, or imagine we need, physical intimacy with another person when we have not fully grown up and when we retain vestiges of the dependence we had as children. Intimacy of a sexual nature has the effect of keeping us in an infantile and dependent state, so that we are constantly seeking other people to gratify our own urges. We may then feel deeply disappointed, cheated and frustrated when we are denied this.

As babies, we must necessarily have a very intimate physical relationship with our mothers, or whoever is doing the job of caring, simply in order to survive at all. If this physical closeness were absent, the chances of life being maintained would be slight indeed. Both physically and mentally a baby needs the reassurance of regular bodily contact to thrive and to have a foundation on which to establish later independence. Physical contact between mother and baby is observable throughout the animal kingdom and all immature creatures must have this closeness. As we grow up, our need for physical contact with our parents lessens all the time. A child of three likes lots of hugs and kisses, but a 15-year-old will feel distinctly embarrassed and uncomfortable at being publicly hugged and kissed by either mother or father.

As independence asserts itself and ties with parents become ever looser, another yearning may arise when the adolescent falls in love with someone of similar age to him- or herself. Long before most teenagers actually fall in love with another human being, they have practice runs – fantasy relationships with pop or film stars, or a teacher at school. Posters of the object of affection often adorn the bedrooms of young people but at this stage any thought of physical intimacy is at a rudimentary level; most teenagers in the 14–16 age-group have very little physical contact with anybody at all.

For a time, the young person has no perception of a gap, no idea of a need to be filled. But at a slightly later stage the teenager is liable to fall in love with somebody who is, at least theoretically, more or less attainable.

This falling in love always comes at a time when we perceive a need to break old ties for good, and forge new ones. Intense emotional and physical intimacy will usually ensure that this break takes place. According to American behavioural scientists Karen and Kenneth Dion, the romantic relationship usually blossoms at 'the interstices of institutional systems, or at transition times between major role commitments'. It is extremely rare for anybody to fall in love at other times, according to recent scientific research.

When we fall in love, we do not normally think much more about our parents. They are no longer so all-important, such all-pervasive influences. The one-time closeness of that particular bond is now at an end; it is simply not needed any more. Those who are unable to form close relationships with members of the opposite sex are very often people who are continuing unnaturally close relationships with their parents. The man who never seems to fall in love is often a permanent 'Mummy's boy'. Conversely, those who are having sex or who get married at a very young age are almost always people who come from broken homes or have had an unsatisfactory relationship with their parents for a long time.

The break with parents – with the old, now outdated mode of living – is made possible, indeed virtually forced, by physical and emotional intimacy with another person from the peer group.

During the initial, heady stage of being in love, sex may often be unavoidable, even necessary, to enable people to commit themselves to each other and finally to cut the 'apron strings'.

All sex researchers have noted that in the early stages of a relationship sex tends to be very frequent indeed, and both partners enjoy and demand it equally. In fact, during the first year, each is liable to experience severe withdrawal symptoms if sex, for some reason, cannot take place. The deprived partners may imagine they cannot even get through the night alone. When a relationship is first established, the lovers may well feel that sex and emotional intimacy are one and the same thing. They may wake each other up several times during the night for the sheer bliss of making love. It is as if their appetites for each other, their longing to be together, and to merge into each other, can never be satisfied.

Then, inexplicably and very gradually, it all starts to fade. Both partners find, at some stage, that they no longer have quite the same overpowering urge to spend each minute in the other's company. They are perfectly happy to be apart on occasion. They also discover, often to their intense annoyance, that they are less keen on sex with each other. In most cases, intercourse takes place far less frequently after the first year of a relationship.

The falling-off in frequency is usually very dramatic, from three or four times a week to perhaps once a week or less. The big mistake many people make here is to assume that the new lack of desire for sex means that there is something wrong with the relationship, that the 'magic' has gone out of it. They believe they should now do all they can to bring that initial heady excitement back, so that they can experience that transcendence which was there without effort at first. Psychologists and sex counsellors have mistakenly proposed that at this stage, when two lovers no longer take quite such exclusive delight in each other's company, every effort must be made to 'bring back the romance', to turn each other on again, as happened so naturally in those early days.

It is of course, impossible to bring back the 'romance', however that may be defined. Quite simply, the earlier joy experienced in the presence of the other person has gone because there is no need for it any more. The couple has successfully established a relationship, broken links with the former lifestyle, claimed and won its prize.

The contest is over, so there is no need to keep entering the race time and again. Both partners, if they were honest, would acknowledge that as the years go by, the physical side becomes ever less important, more empty and meaningless. Couples who attempt to turn the clock back, to recreate a memory, are doomed to disappointment because they are resorting to artificiality. When couples desperately try to liven up their marriage by having more sex, trying out more positions, or even by taking other partners, what they are really saying is that their relationship has got stuck: they are playing the same gramophone record over and over again. Instead, they should be accepting that their relationship has moved into a new phase.

Though we know intuitively that this is so, we seem to find it hard to accept that, once gone, the old feeling never will return. We like to pretend, against all reason and evidence, that if we try hard enough the original intensity can be recaptured. It is at this rather desperate stage that couples may try candlelit dinners, 'erotic' underwear, waterbeds, pink lighting for the bedroom or 'marital aids', and then wonder why, despite all this extra effort, they both continue to feel empty inside.

It is as if they were taking part in a charade, watching themselves acting but knowing that their hearts are no longer in it. The wife in the old joke who says during intercourse, 'Sam, the ceiling needs painting' has been held up as the supreme example of callousness on the part of women. But the reason the joke worked is because it is true. It is actually impossible to be sexually excited by a partner once you have been married for five years or more.

When this stage is reached, a sensible couple would admit to each other and themselves that their relationship needed to be redefined, on a different footing. But most of us are not sensible, and want to keep experiencing an adolescent excitement that was actually a part of growing up, a process rather than a stable, permanent condition.

When a couple's sex life becomes reduced to a mere remnant of what it was, that is the time when many partners start to have affairs, or even look for another person with whom to share their life. But all are only short-term solutions because eventually, the same boredom will set in again, however exciting and 'different' the new person may seem at first. A relationship that is based on the physical compatibility of two disparate individuals will always become less and less intimate as time goes on because, once the physical side has lost its attraction, there will be precious little else.

People who look to sex to fulfil deep needs for intimacy are going to be eluded all their lives, as they are searching in the wrong way. The physical act can never establish true closeness with another person. Those who sorely miss the wonderful romantic feeling of chase and capture, the stuff of every romantic novel, may have many, many affairs, all in an effort to regain that feeling of bliss and transcendence. But in reality this mission is doomed. The liaisons are likely to be extremely unsatisfactory and the quester's deep inner loneliness will continue.

Sex can never be a magic cure for boredom, as it is never possible to cure a deeply-felt malaise by physical means. At best, it is a diversion that will eventually only exacerbate the feelings of loneliness, inadequacy and frustration which lie underneath. Looking to sex will only make you crave it more, and thus feel deprived when it is not forthcoming.

Sex can all too easily become a habit. If you have got used to including it in your daily routine, you may miss it if it is not there. Most married couples who continue to have sex do so, it must be said, out of sheer habit rather than any stronger emotion. They believe it is necessary because, right from the start, it has been an ingredient of their relationship with each other, and they cannot imagine relating to each other in any other way.

Sex can act as a trigger mechanism to get people out of one type of relationship and into another. There is no denying that at first, with a new and very attractive partner, sex can seem like an uplifting, spiritual experience, momentarily transcending space and time. It can appear to be a means of transporting individuals into a new and more wonderful dimension, and feelings of relief, release and satisfaction, which the brain interprets as bliss, may suffuse the system.

Partners often lean on each other while they are sorting out themselves and their relationship. During that time, it can be very comforting and reassuring to know that your love is returned. Hugs, kisses and sexual intercourse are part of this physical interaction. But in time the need for these experiences becomes rather like wearing spectacles or walking with a crutch all your life. If possible, you should not rely on this support forever as there may well come a time when it is not available.

Also, after a time, continuing to interact sexually may actually work to stop personal growth, as it renders you continually bound to another person. If the need for dependence has ended, the need for a sexual liaison may also have ended: the important thing is to be able to recognize this.

Intimacy, as so far defined, should ideally be seen as a growth process and a stepping stone, rather than a way of life in itself.

Once two people who are close to each other are able to relinquish their reliance on sex, genuine intimacy, of the kind that really matters, may flourish. Most long-term married couples continue to have sex but have long lost any real sense of companionship. This is observable when they are on holiday together, or having dinner: more often than not, they do not have a word to say to each other. Yet, when they are in their hotel bedroom, sex is almost certain to take place, its sole function being to keep the partners bound to each other in a kind of mutual hostility.

True intimacy occurs when people feel supremely at ease in each other's company, free of embarrassment, with no need to hold back. In such circumstances innermost thoughts, feelings, hopes and desires can be discussed in the full knowledge that the other person will understand and that confidences will never be broken, trust never betrayed. This emotional intimacy, which is precious and life-enhancing, can never be brought about, increased or made more intense by physical sex.

Certainly for women the very thought of sex is liable to inhibit true intimacy with a man. They may worry that, if they open up their hearts, their partners may take this to mean they are willing to open their legs as well. Unless this is what they want, the very possibility can make them become cold, distant and afraid.

Ann Landers, America's most popular agony aunt, has revealed in a new survey that most women prefer a cuddle to sex anyway. She said: 'The importance of sex is overrated – women want affection.' In her survey, of more than 64,000 readers of her column, over 72 per cent of women said they far preferred affectionate hugs and kisses to sex. Ann Landers said that her letters indicated that the average man tended to use sex purely as physical release. 'It has no more significance than a sneeze,' she said.

Women often worry that if they refuse sex their partners will lose interest in them very quickly. It is this very fear which frequently makes middle-aged women continue to agree to sex when it has long become for them an empty act, devoid of meaning. However, women also fear that if they do not agree to sex they will lose all the loving hugs, kisses and close physical contact that they do still enjoy.

Psychologists and psychiatrists are now starting to come to the conclusion that sex and intimacy have very little to do with each other. Dr David Smail, a professor of psychology at Nottingham University, has said that his work with severely depressed NHS patients, who are often given sex therapy for their problems, has led him to believe that sex is in reality deeply unsatisfying, and a poor substitute for true intimacy. 'Sex has become our sad, misguided substitute for true intimacy,' he stated in a *Guardian* interview; he further observed that when people attempt to satisfy a spiritual and emotional need with a physical act they are inevitably leaving that deeper need unsatisfied.

Dr Garth Wood, who trained as a psychiatrist at the Royal Free Hospital, London, declared recently in an essay entitled *Sex and Love: the Crisis of Expectation* that sex is now seen, entirely mistakenly, as the fount of ultimate pleasure and as a God-given right for everybody. His view is that humans do not need sex at all, as there are other, far better ways of showing love and affection.

'We must revalue sex in the hierarchy of human activities and reassess its place,' he recommends. Then, he believes, many 'problems' now associated with sexual dysfunction would simply vanish. 'Frigid' women would become normal, as indeed they are. 'We scratch and scrape to satisfy libidinous urges,' contines Dr Wood, but 'the time has now come to declare war on such dangerous and misleading ideas, and to recognize that life is not about the search for short-term pleasure.' Sex, Dr Wood claims, is far too often a short-term 'fix' at the expense of longer-term contentedness. In our society, we have taken on board the wrong idea that everybody is owed a full and satisfying sex life.

'We indulge in lusts which contravene conscience, and we pay in guilt,' he writes. Casual sexual activity serves only to make the guilt worse, and adds to the already heavy burden of worry most of us carry around.

Ordinary people are now also realizing that, if they can become celibate, that this does not mean saying goodbye to intimate relationships, with either sex.

The following are case histories of people who at some stage in their lives decided to have a period of celibacy; each of them discovered that it enhanced, rather than ruined, their close, important relationships.

PETER, a 30-year-old musician, felt that a time of celibacy was important to enable him to progress in his career. He said: 'Most musicians and, in fact, all creative people, can find it difficult to sustain permanent relationships.

'There is no doubt in my mind that physical sex gets in the way of creativity, yet, before becoming celibate myself, I would say that at least 75 per cent of my time was spent thinking about sex.

'From the age of about 20, when all my friends seemed to be pairing off, I longed to find a permanent girlfriend and have transcendent sex. But I came to realize that marriage was actually the last thing I wanted for myself, at least then. Yet because of society's conditioning I felt I was missing out by not having a long-term physical relationship.

'So I embarked on a series of sexual liaisons, but soon discovered that those I had never led to a depth of emotional feeling. Rather, they clouded it, because sex ended up being a game between the two of us, which revolved around the physical needs and expectations of both of us.

'I now have an extremely close relationship with a woman, but it is completely non-physical. I'm closer to her, though, than to any other human being, and we can talk about whatever comes into our heads. There is no reticence whatever between us, and no physical desire on either side. We can, as a result, feel supremely at ease in each other's company, and the fact that there is no physical basis for the relationship – and never will be – actually enables us to be closer emotionally.

'When you are in love, and have ideals, you find that these can never be met by another person in a physical way. They can't be. It's only on the mental level that true closeness can ever occur. I worried for a time, when I became celibate, that this would mean I had no close relationships any more, but in fact I've found it so freeing. As I'm not bound up in a physical way with another person, I've now come closer to a larger number of people, and have far more friends.'

CELIA, a 40-year-old married woman who has enjoyed, by mutual consent, a celibate relationship with her husband for the past two years, said: 'I had a very strong feeling that I was growing out of sex. It was great when we were young, – we were teenage lovers – but over the years, our once-loving sex life had dwindled into a matter of habit and obligation. I realized that when we were making love we were really trying to recapture what had happened at first.

'My husband was willing to give celibacy a try and we've both found that since our physical life finished we have actually become far better friends with each other. We talk more, open up our hearts more and are like two grown-ups, rather than teenagers playing games. We can be closer because there is no longer anger, jealousy or lust coming between us.

'After a time of not having sex, I came to realize just how much habit is ingrained, and that it is quite unrelated to true expressions of love.

'Neither of us is going around in a perpetual agony of lust and sexual frustration. We came to realize that the sex urge, if not fed regularly, simply dies away, like a fire that is not stoked up. I'm not saying that John and I will be celibate for ever, but the break from sex has given us the opportunity to develop new respect for each other. And neither of us has had affairs during this time – we just haven't felt the need.'

JULIA, a 26-year-old single university lecturer, said: 'You soon come to realize that a relationship without sex is quite different from one in which sex is important. With the latter, everything culminates in making love. For most people, when you meet another person your initial thought about them is expressed in terms of sex – as to whether or not you fancy them. If you regard yourself as unattractive, as I did, you tend to imagine nobody would ever want to go to bed with you.

'This was my problem for a long time. As I have always regarded myself as plain. I didn't think anybody would ever fall in love with me. As a result, my self-respect was low and I was a wallflower, shy and unobserved, at parties.

'I realized that all the sex I was having was getting me nowhere, and was actually making me even more nervous, lonely and afraid. I've been far stronger in myself since deciding on a time of celibacy, and I have become more able to form proper relationships, where there can be genuine loving and giving.

'But once I was aware that I could be a friend, that I didn't always have to prove myself as a bed partner, I discovered that I could have a far better relationship with my colleagues, most of whom are male. I think they also found it a relief that I wasn't wanting to get them into bed, and that made them more willing to talk to me. If you don't want a sex partner, you actually put out different vibrations, and these are picked up by other people. It sounds odd, perhaps, but it does work. I've now got lots of close friends but no bed partners, and I haven't got the impression that I am missing something valuable.'

MARGARET, a successful novelist with two failed marriages behind her, eventually came to feel there was not room in her life for a demanding physical relationship as well as her career.

She said: 'When I had physical relationships, I realized I was just exhausted all the time. I didn't know I was exhausted until I decided on a period of celibacy and then discovered how much better I felt. It wasn't just the physical act of sex that was so tiring, but the amount of giving. For a woman, making love involves a lot of giving – this doesn't happen so much with a man – and making sacrifices. In every sexual relationship that exists, you find that one person is giving and the other is taking. It's usually the woman who gives. And all this giving means that you have less time left over for yourself.

'I don't feel now that I need sex, though whether I shall be celibate for the rest of my life, of course I can't say.'

We all know that non-sexual physical intimacy can happen in close-knit families, with long-term friends and with colleagues; this can be extended into relationships with those members of the opposite sex for whom we feel affection but would not want sexual involvement.

Couples who no longer have sex can still give and receive physical affection. In such cases it is more likely to be genuine affection, an expression of fondness for the other person that has no expectations of intercourse, or 'satisfying needs', attached to it.

CHAPTER 9

Celibacy and creativity

The question of whether celibacy contributes to, or detracts from, creativity is a difficult one to answer. I know that as soon as I say a positive commitment to celibacy makes a person more creative, there will be ferocious attempts to shoot my argument down in flames.

For though many great creative artists of the past have been celibate, an equal – possibly greater – number were emphatically not. Great painters whose lives were not celibate include Picasso, Modigliani, Gauguin, Rodin and Augustus John. Among the celibate, one thinks of Botticelli and Andy Warhol.

Poets, too, have not seemed noticeably greater in accordance with whether or not they lived celibate lives. The great non-celibate poets include Donne, Coleridge, Shelley and Browning, while Alexander Pope, Gerard Manley Hopkins and Keats – possibly more by accident than design – are among the celibates.

The astute reader will have noticed that all the names I have mentioned so far are male. Among highly creative females, one will find a far higher proportion of celibates: Jane Austen, Emily Dickinson, the Brontës and Stevie Smith are just a few examples.

And here we have the nub of the matter, I think. Though sexuality does not in itself confer or remove creativity, we have to be aware that if sexual satisfaction gives something to one partner, then it must take away the same amount from the other. Very many great painters, writers and musicians of the past have been ruthless exploiters of women, and have had many mistresses they treated more or less badly. Great artists, composers and poets are often people who are overflowing with creativity, and expression of their sexuality is just one aspect of this.

In his biography of Augustus John, Michael Holroyd

describes how John would often pounce on his female models and have, or attempt to have, sexual intercourse with them before he started painting them. In this way, he was making the model 'his', possessing her and at the same time infusing himself with some of her essence, her individuality. It is therefore easy to understand that he gained psychic strength from the liaison. What is more difficult to explain is exactly what benefit the model herself received from the sexual act – as with the young women who slept non-sexually with the aged Gandhi. True, the model was going to be immortalized on canvas in a flattering, or at least interesting, painting. But in giving herself sexually to the artist she was losing some of her own being, and risking becoming known as Augustus John's mistress rather than as a person in her own right.

One of the weaknesses of women down the ages is that we have allowed ourselves, even been willing, to sacrifice our own creativity to that of men, assuming the creations of males to be greater. What we have lost they have gained, so in many cases it could be said that they have increased their artistic powers at our expense.

My argument is that women will not and cannot become creative in their own right until they can learn to use their powers for their own advancement, rather than so lightheartedly donating them to the men in their lives. One way in which they can maintain and increase their own creativity is by becoming celibate – not necessarily for ever and ever, but specifically in order to increase their personal creativity and powers of self-expression.

Men would also gain from this. There is no evidence whatever that celibate artists have been lesser geniuses because they did not have sexual intercourse with women: rather the reverse, perhaps, because celibate artists are those people who are more complete in themselves, and who look inside themselves rather than hoping to gain inspiration from others.

The idea that periods of celibacy are needed for great creative efforts is a very ancient one, and is enshrined in all the old religions. In the twentieth century we have tended to forget that there is any association between celibacy and creativity, and have brought about the mistaken idea that in order to maximize the creative urge we must embark on the freest possible sexual expression.

In Victorian days it was seriously believed that a man had only a certain amount of sperm to spend, and that if he was profligate with this he could expect other activities – non-sexual ones – to suffer. The belief was that sexual energy detracted from energy needed for other activities and impeded their chances of coming to fruition. This idea has survived to our own day, in rather diluted form, in the world of sport.

Leading boxers are always holed up in a hotel for at least two weeks before a major fight, and are not allowed sexual contact even with their wives. During this time they are always closely watched by their coaches to make sure a hundred-per-cent effort is put into their training, and that they are not diverted by other, more frivolous, pursuits. After the fight is over, of course, they can indulge all they like. Presumably sports coaches have good reasons for insisting on this pre-match celibacy. They know that sexual activity drains the available resources and that every man, even a world-class boxing champion, has only so much strength.

We know that production of sperm, which is composed mainly of protein, takes a lot of bodily effort and that supply of the raw materials needed to manufacture sperm is not inexhaustible. In manufacturing sperm, the body is necessarily taking protein and materials away from other sources. When sex is frequent and prolonged the body may in time lose valuable amounts of trace minerals and be permanently depleted.

The ancient idea that sexual intercourse actually inhibits creativity is also found in the psychic and spiritualist worlds. Psychics are people who believe they have extra powers of perception, and can therefore sense things that the ordinary person is unable to. Many psychics nowadays operate as 'spiritual healers' and say that in order to operate what they term the healing channel and get a clear line through to God, the spirit world or the universal unconsciousness they must be celibate. Most are not lifelong celibates, but they prepare themselves for a healing session in much the same way as a world-class sportsman prepares himself for a major event. For a few days beforehand they will withdraw from contact with others, eat a very light diet, usually meatless, abstain from alcohol and make sure they have as little disturbance as possible from outside sources.

Most psychics say they have learned from experience that unless they do this their powers desert them. It is significant that most of the great female mediums of the past and present have been post-menopausal, and therefore able to direct more energy to their psychic and creative development than if they were involved with a sex life and reproduction. One practising medium told me that few women realized they possessed psychic powers until they were well into their forties.

Very many people, she went on to say, were aware of psychic abilities as children. With adolescence, however, and the dawning of sexuality, these powers seemed to disappear, and they came back only when sex was no longer a factor in their lives. Male mediums have largely said the same thing, that they noticed there was something different about them as children, but that whatever unusual abilities they may have had when young deserted them as manhood approached. What they came to understand later, however, was that these powers had not actually deserted them but went into abeyance. They could not compete with sexuality.

Everybody who is creative operates, at least to some extent, on a psychic level. Great scientists and inventors have often spoken of the sudden flash, the *eureka*, that instantly makes everything fall into place. However, this flash never happens completely out of the blue, but always occurs when the mind has been occupied with the problem for a long time. Any genuine creative effort, even when it seems like sudden inspiration, is actually the result of prolonged concentration and attention to the matter in hand. What we call genius is the ability to give such individed attention: no creation worth the name will come into being without it.

Some spiritually-minded people say that when we are being creative we are connecting ourselves to a higher power and are receiving energy from God. To be truly creative, such thinkers believe, we have to direct our search upward, not downwards to the genital area. Inspiration does not lie there. Creativity is lost when our energies are diffused and diverted into too many areas at once.

Bernard Shaw, who ranks among the great celibates, once said that the genuine artist will make his old mother go out to work at 70, and will be capable of committing any unsocial action so long as it enables him to further his art and express himself. What he meant was that nothing should be allowed to come between a true artist and his artistic expression.

We can never know, of course, whether the great artists of the past would have been any greater if they had been celibate, or if they had been more inclined towards the celibate state. But we do have to consider whether any form of artistic expression is worth the price of the destruction of another human being. When Amadeo Modigliani died, of poverty and disease, his mistress Jeanne, then seven months pregnant with her second child, committed suicide. When Lytton Strachey died, a woman called Carrington who had worshipped him for many years shot herself. When Arthur Koestler realized he was suffering from an incurable disease he committed suicide. His wife Cynthia died with him at the same time. These women – and there are many more examples – had given their all to very clever, very talented and very creative men, instead of working at developing their own creativity. In the examples given, Jeanne, Modigliani's mistress, was an art student and Carrington was also an artist in her own right. But the only reason we remember them is because they were associated with famous men.

We admire the novel *Tender Is the Night* by Scott Fitzgerald, about a psychiatrist and his mentally unstable wife, but would his wife Zelda have become so mentally unbalanced if Fitzgerald had not ruthlessly plundered her personality and her life for 'material'? The men I have mentioned so far were supremely talented and inspired devotion. But when you devote yourself to another person you will gradually lose your own qualities, for these will become submerged. Any woman who 'gives herself' sexually to another person risks losing, in time, all her own individual powers. It can be argued that most of the great artists of the past have been male simply because women have always given up their own sexual and psychic energies to men. Scott Fitzgerald went so far as to say to his wife – who had dreams of becoming a novelist herself – '*I* am the novelist.' This gave him, as he saw it, every right to use Zelda as his material, but he left her no equal right to make use of the same information in her own creative work.

If we, as men and women, want to increase our own creative powers without destroying the other people in our lives, then we should consider the possibility of using periods of celibacy in order to increase powers of concentration, to look into ourselves, to become introspective and not to let our finite amounts of energy drain away into pursuits that have no end product and no personal long-term benefit.

An American woman, Dana Densmore, has argued persuasively that for women there is a positive connection between celibacy and creativity. Founder of the Artemis Institute, which teaches 'self-empowerment' and self-realization, she writes:

Celibacy is choosing a life of autonomy, responsibility for oneself, precious solitude and an undiluted devotion of one's energies to the work one has at hand. The celibate woman chooses to put her time, energy and sense of self into her own development and her own work rather than putting those things into a sexual relationship with another person.

Sometimes celibacy is a choice for life but more often it is a choice made for a period of time, lasting as long as the benefits and pleasures of celibacy outweigh the pleasures and benefits which can be offered by its alternatives.

In other words, she says, one does not need to commit oneself to lifelong, nun-like celibacy in order to realize one's creative potential. Rather, one should realize that any genuine creative effort in itself takes a huge amount of energy and that the end product will always be better if a hundred-per-cent concentration can be given at the crucial time. Such intense effort is not needed, nor would it be possible, all the time.

Dana Densmore continues in her essay, printed in the American journal *The Celibate Woman*:

Celibacy is sometimes embarked on as a negative condition. It can also be used as an exercise in self-mastery (it has this function for men more often than for women). Or one may feel one is sacrificing an imagined satisfaction in deference to moral or spiritual dictates, to punish oneself, or out of a sense of self-disgust. Or, one may withdraw from sexual involvement in reaction against the disappointments in relationships.

But celibacy can be, and more often is, a positive choice. It releases time, energy and solitude that are helpful for almost all pieces of work and essential for some.

The process of self-empowerment is the one piece of work for which celibacy is particularly useful.

It is not possible, of course, to become creative unless there is power there; why not, asks Densmore, harness it instead of allowing it to drain uselessly away?

Falling in love, claims Densmore, is remarkably easy, whereas becoming powerful is very hard work. Being in love is absorbing and ecstatic and can blind a person agreeably to the ways in which responsibility for individual empowerment may have been abdicated. However, falling in love and abandoning oneself to another person always lead to disappointments, and as Dorothy Parker said, if two people imagine they are truly equally and ecstatically in love, 'one of you is lying'.

Solitude, declares Dana Densmore, is essential for the self-empowerment process to take place and it cannot be achieved at the same time as a passionate love affair. Through celibacy, one can get used to, and come to enjoy, periods of solitude – periods in which one can 'find oneself'. Until this happens, nobody can become creative.

Creativity takes conscious effort, and does not mean abandoning oneself to passions and swings of mood. Even those who believe true creativity wells out of the unconscious understand that the unconscious has to be put in touch with the conscious before the projected poem, painting or piece of sculpture can become a reality. We also have to know how to tap the unconscious.

Whenever we are caught up in either casual or committed love-type relationships, we inevitably have less time available for ourselves and for solitary pursuits. The time given to relationships can make all the difference, according to Dana Densmore, between doing something meaningful in our self-development work and our life work and being too swamped even to keep up with the laundry. The demands of love relationships, she says, make great inroads into our reserves of energy. Lovers do more than take up time: they involve and affect our sense of self, and as affairs are usually so intimate and absorbing, they can leave little time or inclination for anything else. A person who is not powerful is always vulnerable to taking on somebody else's reality. In an intimate relationship it becomes necessary to enter into the other person's unconscious up to a point, and to consider his or her point of view. In the intensity of intimate relationships, it is easy to forget the importance of one's own work and simply take on the burden of helping somebody else to achieve.

The writer and lawyer John Mortimer has described in his autobiography *Clinging to the Wreckage* how his mother – herself an artist before her marriage – took on the 'extraordinary bondage' of accompanying her blind barrister husband to work every day on the train and colluding in the pretence that he was not really blind at all. Mortimer writes that he thought his mother might take up her art again once she became a widow, but adds that she never did. She, like so many women, had – possibly perfectly willingly – abandoned her sense of self to become an extra, and essential, limb to her husband. In enabling him to remain powerful, she neglected her own creative talents.

In talking about the importance of celibacy and the realization of individual creative powers, I am of course referring to celibacy in its widest interpretation: not simply abstinence from sexual intercourse, but from the idea that you 'need' another person – a lover, a husband or wife, to complete you. There is, as was pointed out earlier, little difference between technical celibacy and spending all one's time looking for the love of one's life. The relationship between Carrington and Lytton Strachey did not involve much – if any – physical sex, as Strachey was homosexual and Carrington herself had an aversion to the sexual act. But she gave herself to him just as surely as if there had been sexual involvement. Sexual involvement does not only mean genital coupling; it means relying on somebody else, needing to be part of a couple, looking to be loved and needed.

Dana Densmore writes that many people enter into sexual relationships not because they are overflowing with lust and passion, but because they are afraid of being alone, of having nobody who will love them and care about them. In fact, she says, the person who has made a positive commitment to celibacy for the purposes of increasing self-power and creativity finds she or he has *more* friends and becomes more popular, simply because an aura of autonomy, achievement, confidence and strength, rather than one of weakness and dependence, has been generated. We all like to have relationships with strong, reliable, autonomous individuals who do not drain us, who do not make demands, but instead are able to give. The lack of that exclusive tie-up with just one other person releases more energy for others and other activities. Dana Densmore concludes her article on celibacy and power by saying: 'The powerful person, after all, is not interested in wasting her time on casual relationships undertaken for entertainment, sensory stimulation or ego satisfaction.'

Countless male psychologists, 'sexperts' and biographers have drawn attention to the wide discrepancy between male and female achievement in the world of art, science, music and literature, and have tried to explain why this should be. There is little argument but that women are as intelligent as men, equally capable of grasping abstract concepts, and, certainly as children, equally creative. It was found, for instance, that once women were allowed to take competitive exams, they surprised and disconcerted the male students by coming top. Yet though we have had over a hundred years of female education to university level, and there are now, theoretically at least, equal opportunities for women, women are still not achieving the same status in the professions and the arts as men.

To many male writers there is an extremely simple explanation for this: women can create, without any effort at all, new life – that is, babies; they are therefore achieving supreme heights of creativity anyway and so do not need to paint, write or sculpt in order to prove further their ability to create. There has even been a school of thought which propounds that male creations are a feeble attempt to emulate women's natural creativity.

I do not begin to subscribe to this argument. I see it as part of a male conspiracy to keep women in their place and content with a passive, dependent role.

Every female animal – human or otherwise – is born with the innate capacity to create new life. Every woman, apart from the infertile, can all too easily become pregnant and give birth. The act is not creative in itself as it demands no personal effort, no individual qualities, no education, concentration or native talent. The simplest uneducated peasant woman can just as successfully create new life as can a highly educated university graduate. It may be argued that bringing up children is a creative act, but again, children will grow up whether or not they have a 'creative' mother. A woman does not have control over her children. Though it is often said (erroneously) that the hand that rocks the cradle rules the world, there is no direct and necessary correlation between the way a child is brought up and the way it eventually turns out. One can see this very clearly in almost every family where children born to the same parents, living in the same house and brought up in practically identical ways, nevertheless turn out very different, as different as any random selection of people. A mother may make great efforts to bring up her children correctly, but she has very little control over their eventual personalities or what they do with their lives.

Any type of woman at all can become a mother: no special qualities are needed to perform this role. One does not have to be specially loving, or kindly, or nurturing. Perhaps to do it *well* requires effort but a large body of evidence points to the idea that the more children are left to their own devices, the less damage will be caused and the less warped their adult personalities will be.

Another aspect of child-rearing is that mothers who focus their attention entirely on their children to the neglect of their own personal growth and advancement may be bereft, and feel that life is purposeless, once their children eventually leave home.

The most creative pursuit any individual can undertake is that of self-discovery; it is difficult to discover yourself and to find out exactly who you are when you are continuously trying – and failing – to satisfy other people's needs. Those who believe that creative energy can be increased through sexual activity should remind themselves of the universal law which says that energy can be neither created nor destroyed, only transferred. When artists – in the widest sense of that word – have many mistresses, what they are doing is transferring, or attempting to transfer, psychic energy from the women to themselves. This is one definition of inspiration. But in taking this energy, they are necessarily depleting the woman's own personal stores of energy. It is very rare that the mistresses of famous artists have been equal artists in their own right, because they would not have had the energy both to give to their man and to be autonomously creative. For many of these women, the only time they were able to achieve in their own right was once the relationship was over.

One reason why creative artists have been more libertine throughout the ages than, say, accountants, is because in certain professions there is no necessity for energies to be transferred in order for work to be done. But the artist is restless, exploitative and ruthless. Most artists, as their widows and mistresses have often revealed later, are hell to live with, but have usually been spared the censure that might have applied to less creative people. Their behaviour could be excused if they nevertheless produced sublime creations.

In the past, many women have been content, or have at least accepted, a secondary, passive role in artistic creation. Instead of being novelists, poets, architects, musicians and so on ourselves, we have been willing to settle for the task of being wife or mistress to men who occupy such roles.

But if we women withdraw our sexual energies from other people and put that same energy into our own development, we can be as creative and original as any man in the past. Men will then have to find another source of inspiration, and instead of looking to the genital area look upwards, to their own minds and brains and beyond. The inspiration which comes from these sources can be infinite – and not temporary, as is the case when one tries to gain energy from another person.

We know that all too many male artists have achieved their creations at the cost of leaving a trail of devastation and wrecked lives in their wake, and in some cases even self-destruction. This is largely, though not entirely, of course, due to their trying to wrest their energy from material and sensual sources. Alcohol, drugs, women – all serve a purpose, but all these roads to the unconscious are doomed to end in chaos.

If men are not able to draw on women's psychic energies through sexual exploitation and appropriation, one immediate result will be less pornography. American writers such as Harold Robbins, Norman Mailer and Henry Miller – all women-haters, at least in their fiction – have added to the sum of pornography in the world, for they have portrayed women as sexual, half-human objects suitable for degradation and exploitation. In the novels of these men, sex, violence and rape are all part of the high-selling package. Unfortunately, clever female authors such as Erica Jong have copied them – but women do not find that writing pornography comes naturally to them.

One way that non-creative men have often tried to gain extra powers for themselves is through witchcraft. Some imagine that this is old-hat, never practised now and is in any case confined to Dennis Wheatley novels. This is far from being the case. The old idea of the female virgin sacrifice, as expounded in Dennis Wheatley's *To the Devil – a Daughter*, is by no means only fantasy fiction. It still goes on. Apparently witchcraft flourished in Nazi Germany; more recently a form of it was practised in the 1960s in Britain by the osteopath Stephen Ward and the so-called members of the 'Cliveden set', who would go to Lord Astor's country home at weekends and perform orgies which had the effect of increasing male power – for a time. It seems that one reason why Stephen Ward was able to inveigle his way into high society was through his use of witchcraft: he tapped into sexual powers that were released during the orgies. Ward was not himself sexual; according to the memoirs of Christine Keeler, he slept with women quite chastely, but nevertheless he used their powers to turn himself from an ordinary, undistinguished little man into somebody special. The price he paid was suicide, of course. When these powers are tapped in an artificial way, they can never do good.

Witchcraft has lasted through the ages because it undoubtedly does work for a time. The dances, incantations, frenzies and sacrifices do result in a potent transference of energy. But unless the energy is obtained by good means, it will turn on the person and destroy everybody involved.

Good and evil are not outside entities but manifestations of creative energies that are inside all of us, and energy which is obtained by evil means can only have an evil outcome. If sex were, as some people like to believe, normal and healthy, a mainly good activity, it could not be harnessed in this way, for evil and wrongdoing. But we all know that it can.

Many satanist stories and horror films of the *Brides of Dracula* type are basically about transferring energy from somebody good – i.e. the virgin – into somebody evil, such as the vampire. The ancient folklore belief that there is something both good and powerful about virginity persists. If it did not, these potent horror fantasies would not be woven around the idea of the virgin sacrifice.

Sexuality is not the only source of creativity, nor is it the best one. The idea that sexuality equals creativity has come about because we have confused the mechanical means of creating life with mental creativity. When an egg and a sperm meet and are fertilized, that is simply a biological event, and there is no connection whatever with the process which sets a work of art into being.

CHAPTER 10

Celibacy and food

For very many years it was assumed that food was just fuel for the body and that as long as there was adequate intake of proteins, carbohydrates and fats it did not much matter what was eaten. The important thing was to get a good balance of nutrients.

Now we know differently. The vast amount of research conducted over the past few years into food and its relationship to health has revealed that in very many ways the food we eat is directly related to both behaviour and physical condition. We know, for example, that hyperactive children often improve considerably when given a natural diet free from artificial flavourings and colourings.

It also seems likely that there are definite links between criminal behaviour and the kind of food eaten. The main work in this area has been carried out by an American scientist, Dr Alexander Schauss, who found that a high proportion of people committing serious crimes were eating a diet composed mainly of junk foods. Junk foods, he concluded, are liable to affect behaviour adversely.

Schauss discovered that the worst offender was sugar, and that very many criminals were addicted to huge quantities of the stuff, usually the white refined variety, which comes to us stripped of essential nutrients. A chronic deficiency of these nutrients can lead to irritability, depression and hostility towards others, according to reports.

Potential criminals, says Schauss, are those who are easily angered, unduly sensitive to criticism, easily irritated and hostile and aggressive. Sugar and other over-refined foods can make their behavioural problems worse by causing fluctuating blood-sugar levels, which in turn leads to violent mood swings – periods of over-excitability followed by depression.

In the UK John Lester, a retired doctor who has been researching into the connection between diet and behaviour, believes that junk foods in the diet can cause serious behavioural problems. In a recent interview he told me: 'At first, there was enormous resistance to my ideas but now people are starting to come round. It was initially very difficult to convince anybody that junk food could upset the system, but people have been converted now by the evidence.'

In the three years Dr Lester has spent working at Basingstoke Hospital with children who have serious behavioural problems, he has discovered: 'They improve considerably on a better diet. I'm now convinced that mental abnormalities can set in through eating the wrong foods. We've got to the state now where we consider that poor health, plus irritability and tension, is actually normal.'

Though there has been great resistance to the idea that diet can adversely affect behaviour, one centre for young offenders in Britain has decided to try the idea. Seventy boys at the Dyson Hall Assessment Centre in Fazackerley, Merseyside, are taking part in a £20,000 experiment to see whether they become less aggressive and less anti-social as a result of following a wholefood, healthy diet.

It now seems almost certain that eating habits can be either a positive or a negative factor in many illnesses, including cancer, heart disease, arthritis, premenstrual tension, anorexia, schizophrenia and many kinds of depression.

More evidence is accumulating all the time to suggest that some foods can be highly arousing to the senses whereas others exert a calming effect. People suffering from serious diseases are now, in the most forward-looking treatment centres, advised to eat foods which are gentle and restorative, and which help the body to regain health. These foods include fresh fruits and vegetables, and sprouted grains. The foods seriously ill patients are advised to avoid include all stimulants, such as tea, coffee and alcohol, and red meat in any but the smallest quantities.

Studies of men and women on vegetarian diets show that they are far less likely to succumb to certain forms of cancer, and are also protected to a certain extent from high blood pressure, strokes and cardiovascular complaints. The reason for this is that vegetarian food is less arousing to the senses than a high-meat diet and therefore puts far less of a strain on the system; moreover, meat and all rich foods can be hard to digest, which means many of the digestive organs have to work harder.

When a person is in a high state of arousal, however this arousal is triggered, vulnerability to all kinds of illnesses, both major and minor, is increased. The heightened arousal in time has the effect of damping down the immune system and making it far less effective at fighting disease. This has been clearly demonstrated in the disease AIDS: all those who succumb to the clinical form of the condition are already under great stress.

So what has all this to do with sex and celibacy? Sex, as we have seen, is in itself a highly arousing activity which increases the quantity of adrenalin and sex hormones that circulate in the system. Since sex became so central to our lives, many of us have been worried if we were not aroused, and may have tried eating and drinking certain substances specifically to increase arousal and sexual interest. What we have often not understood, however, is that this increased arousal can predispose towards certain illnesses by lowering the body's natural resistance. Extra arousal can also make people feel permanently tense and anxious. We may interpret this feeling as either sexual arousal or sexual frustration, but it is certain that the body does not welcome this extra stress.

Countless books and articles have been written on the subject of aphrodisiacs and have given advice as to how we can make ourselves feel 'sexier' – that is, more aroused – by eating certain foods and drinking various stimulating substances. Oysters and other seafoods, raw steak and champagne have all been labelled aphrodisiac, and some people have gone to the lengths of taking mind-altering drugs, such as cocaine, to increase sexual feeling.

Few books, however, have been written on anti-aphrodisiac foods, the ones that can make us feel calm, unaroused, at peace with ourselves. Yet it is the anti-aphrodisiacs we should be consuming, for it is these which are good for both mind and body. The non-aphrodisiac foods are the ones that help to maintain physical health and also guard against the almost permanent feeling of tension which can result from eating foods that over-stimulate the system. Humans are not designed to eat stimulating substances, nor are digestive juices and organs able to cope with them. They are irritants, and that is why they have the effect of setting up strong feelings which we may at various times call passion, excitement, hostility or anger.

Since much of the recent research on the links between nutrition, behaviour and general health has been carried out over the past five years, we have tended to assume this is a completely new science, and that we are now hearing truly revelatory pronouncements. In fact, the idea that foods affect both physical and mental senses is a very ancient one. From the earliest times it has been known that certain foodstuffs were good for maintaining celibacy, contentment and inner peace while others could incite people to violence, anti-social behaviour or, at the very least, extreme irritability.

According to ancient Eastern traditions, there are three distinct categories of food. These are *sattvic* (pure foods); *rajasic* (foods promoting activity and passion); and *tamasic* (foods which encourage dullness, inertia and depression). All the foods we eat predominate in one or other of these qualities, and all have a direct effect on the mind and bodily health.

A *sattvic* diet will help us to attain self-knowledge, peace and understanding, for it both nourishes the body and maintains peace and harmony within the mind. *Sattvic* foods include cereals, wholemeal bread, fresh fruit and vegetables, unsweetened fruit juices, milk, butter and (vegetarian) cheese, nuts, pulses, sprouted grains, honey and herb teas. All these work in harmony with the body to promote a pure and calm mind and enable the system to function at its maximum potential. Those who eat *sattvic* foods will be able to maximize their intelligence and also their effectiveness, according to Eastern tradition. This type of diet leads to true and lasting health as it brings about a balanced flow of energy between body and mind.

The second category, *rajasic*, comprises foods which are

traditionally considered to possess aphrodisiac qualities: very hot, bitter, sour, dry, salty or highly spiced foods. They include sharp spices and strong stimulants such as tea, coffee and alcohol, and also eggs, salt and chocolate. *Rajasic* foods have the effect of ruining the equilibrium of body and mind. They overstimulate the body and excite the passions. Though we have come, in modern times, to view strong, spicy foods as exciting, a 'taste sensation', they in fact make the mind restless and uncontrollable. All violent action, including rape and sexual assault, is *rajasic*, and is partly caused by over-indulgence in foods of this type in cases where the consumer has a susceptibility to such behaviour.

The third type of food, *tamasic*, is the worst, and is not beneficial in any way as it deadens all senses and inhibits reasoning powers and critical faculties. After eating *tamasic* foods, a sense of inertia and misery sets in, and this has the effect of lowering the body's resistance to all kinds of diseases. *Tamasic* foods, which can also cloud the mind with dark, negative emotions, such as anger, greed, lust and jealousy, include meat, onions, garlic, fermented foods such as vinegar, and all stale or overripe substances. Tobacco is also included in this category. A *tamasic* diet can lead to overeating, and is the main cause of obesity.

A *sattvic* diet is totally vegetarian, and excludes not only all meats, fish, poultry and eggs but strongly flavoured vegetables such as onions and garlic. Only a few years ago, such a diet would have been denounced as impossibly cranky, but we are now learning that a vegetarian diet of this type actually has much to recommend it, for both mental and physical well-being.

It has long been a widely held belief that meat excites the passions while a vegetarian diet damps them down. For this reason, vegetarians have in the past been considered rather anaemic, wimpish, not very successful or effective. By contrast, meat-eating has been associated with positive thinking, action, red-bloodedness and vigour. Now, however, science has come to the support of vegetarians with evidence that the passions aroused by meat-eating are actually harmful, both to the meat-eater and those around him or her. One reason why meat can make people angry or violent is that, just before an animal is slaughtered, it knows it is going to die and, in its terror, produces floods of adrenalin. These hormones remain in the carcass meat and can have an adverse effect on the person who eats it. Red meat is far worse in this respect than white meat, as most of the unwanted adrenalin is contained in the bloodstream. Of course, when we eat red meat we also consume a large amount of the animal's blood. In addition to this, factory farming methods make it necessary for the intensively-reared animals to be given large doses of antibiotics, growth hormone and other chemicals, to ensure that they are not too disease-ridden in their artificial living conditions. When we eat factory-farmed meat, we are also eating these antibiotics, which can lower our own resistance to infection.

It could be said that eating lots of red meat makes people sexy. To put it another way, meat makes people more violent, more excitable and more angry – all the emotions that are, in fact, associated with being actively sexy.

Anybody who is serious about wanting to enjoy the positive benefits of celibacy, and would prefer to avoid the disturbing, tension-ridden sensations that are associated with heightened arousal of all kinds, should consider changing from a carnivorous to a vegetarian diet, at the same time avoiding as much artificial, highly processed, food as possible. This is no longer simply the view of what might be considered a cranky minority, but common sense.

It would also be advisable at the same time to phase out or cut down on cigarettes, alcohol, coffee, tea and all other drugs, including where possible medicines from the doctor. All these are artificial substances which arouse the senses and produce tensions in the body. Most people discover, to their delight, that when they change from a meat to a vegetarian diet they are no longer so bothered by negative emotions. At the same time, they become less greedy, are less addicted to the wrong foods, and their sensitivity and powers of perception are increased. As a vegetarian, one is more sensitive to all kinds of subtle vibrations in the atmosphere, to scents, and to the taste of food and drink. One does not so much become excited by food as pleasurably satisfied.

As the new diet is increasingly integrated into everyday life, it will be noticed that energy levels rise and that depression, miseries and groundless fears and anxieties all start to fade away. Along with these will go sexual frustrations and unsatisfiable arousal. Most people find that once they start to eat vegetarian foods the desire to gorge huge steaks, to smoke cigars and drink whisky fades at the same time. It is not so much that a conscious effort is made to give these substances up as that the wish to take them into the system recedes. One simply feels far better without them. Once the mind clears and becomes more alert, sensitive and intelligent, there is also less desire to cloud it again with thoughts of genital sex, which starts to seem sordid and selfish.

Tamasic foods – those in the third category – have the effect of raising blood-sugar levels instantly, with a corresponding let-down a few hours later. This means that blood-sugar levels are in a constant state of flux, and the individual suffers continual tension as a result.

Mahatma Gandhi, who embraced lifelong celibacy from age 36 (see Chapter Three), understood that certain types of food were over-arousing. He said that celibacy was not possible – for a man, at least – unless the celibate ate a pure non-meat diet. He also maintained that much of eating these days had nothing whatever to do with satisfying hunger, and was far more to do with pleasing the palate. The *tamasic* foods, such as sugar, salt and meat, have the added drawback of being highly addictive. Sugar and salt make meals 'tastier' and mean that it is possible to carry on eating huge amounts long after hunger has been satisfied. Greediness in food, as Gandhi knew, easily leads on to greediness in sex, and both in the end drain energy and effectiveness.

Many men find that eating spicy foods makes them excited and can, without any other form of stimulation, produce an embarrassing erection. This can be disturbing, especially if there is no possibility of obtaining sexual release at the time.

Most modern vegetarians eat garlic and onions, so why should these two flavourful vegetables be excluded from the *sattvic* diet? The main reason is that they contain substances which excite the senses. They are highly acidic and can cause internal burning of the mucus membranes. After the digestive process has taken place, substances deriving from onions and garlic settle in the sebaceous glands which are situated just underneath the skin. This is why it is sometimes possible to smell onions and garlic for days after they have been eaten.

In countries where excessive amounts of garlic are consumed, such as Latin America and Spain, people tend to be violent, easily excited and roused to passion, bad-tempered, and suffer from hypertension.

According to the Vedas, ancient Eastern scriptures, onions and garlic have a direct stimulative effect on the male sex organs and, at the same time as arousing sexual interest, lead to increased anger, restlessness and anxiety, especially if there is no way of releasing the sexual tension.

Though there is some scientific evidence to suggest that garlic can protect against heart disease by helping to clear accumulated fat, this protective effect is only applicable to those who are eating too much fat in their diet. It does not protect those who are already eating a low-fat, high-fibre diet. Garlic and onions have no special nutritional value and are not needed by anybody who is already in good health. In both ancient and modern herbals, garlic is listed as a stimulant. Roman soldiers believed it made them fearless, and mythology associates this vegetable with great strength. It is recorded that in Ancient Egypt slaves building the pyramids went on strike in 2,600 BC when their daily garlic allowance was withdrawn, as they then feared they would not have enough strength for their task. It is popularly assumed that vegetarian food is tasteless without onions and garlic, but this is not so. Once these are removed, the subtler flavours of other vegetables will be noticed and appreciated.

Celibacy becomes easier to achieve when following a vegetarian, wholefood diet. But the main benefit is that it renders people less vulnerable to the feelings of frustration and tension that may accompany a high-meat diet. Some people fear that if they become vegetarian, give up alcohol, cigarettes and sex, then everything that makes life exciting and worth living will be removed. In fact this does not happen. Life is just as interesting – perhaps far more so, as the senses will become more alert and keenly tuned – and one's powers of observation and concentration increase. The best aspect is that there is a consciousness of being in charge, rather than being ruled by passions and negative emotions. That in itself promotes confidence, increases intelligence and makes friendships more lasting and meaningful. People on a natural, wholefood diet are less likely to be quarrelsome, argumentative and unduly aggressive.

Such a diet also enables us to start to forget about sex, and to concentrate on those areas of life that may be more worthwhile and rewarding.

CHAPTER 11

Celibacy and the famous

Very often, people who decide to live celibately do so for religious reasons, or in order to dedicate themselves singlemindedly to what they consider a high ideal.

But one does not have to be spiritually-minded in order to live a non-sexual life by choice. Throughout the ages, many people have felt that for them the physical expression of love and affection could be more of a hindrance than a help in their lives. These 'secular celibates' are people who, at some stage in their lives, discover that they do not need such intimate physical interaction with another person and, in fact, do everything they can to avoid it. Sometimes the secular celibates decide to live alone, but in many cases they share their lives in a platonic way with a close friend of the same, or opposite, sex – or even, in some cases, a spouse.

One early example of this is found in the relationship between the philosopher Voltaire and his 'divine Emilie', the Marquise du Chatelet, who was a mathematical and scientific genius in her own right. Their extremely intimate relationship, which often consisted of being alone with each other until the small hours, or all night, was one in which physical sex hardly figured at all. The lack of sex in their relationship meant that Voltaire was able to get to know – and respect – Emilie's mind and intellect, which was on a level with his own.

Emilie and Voltaire both, at different times, had affairs with other people, and Emilie's final affair resulted in her death from childbirth. But it was their relationship with each other that remained central in their lives. Emilie, it must be said, also had a non-sexual relationship with her own husband, the Marquis du Chatelet, after the first few years of marriage.

One of the most famous non-sexual marriages of this century was that of Leonard and Virginia Woolf. The marriage lasted from 1912 until 28 March 1941, when Virginia drowned herself in the river near their home in Sussex. It appears that their marriage was sexual at first, but that Virginia soon grew to dislike sexual intercourse. In their account of the Woolfs' years together, *A Marriage of True Minds*, George Spater and Ian Parsons record that there was, on the part of Virginia, 'a complete affirmative rejection of the sexual act'. The authors add that 'their sex relationship would have unnerved a less resolute character' (than Leonard Woolf). Though physical sex was discontinued not many months after their marriage, their lives together were very happy and content and there is no evidence at all to suggest that Leonard sought sexual satisfaction elsewhere. He lived to be a ripe old age – well over 80 – and was in good health for most of his life: a prime example of the fact that men do not 'need' sex in order to survive, even when it has not been their choice to live celibately.

At first Virginia was very worried about her lack of interest in physical sex. She wrote to a friend, Ka Cox: 'Why do you think people make such a fuss about marriage and copulation? Why do some of our friends change upon losing chastity? Possibly my great age makes it less of a catastrophe [Virginia was aged 30 at the time], but I certainly find the climax immensely exaggerated.'

In his biography of Virginia Woolf, Quentin Bell, her nephew, writes: 'It is a proof of their deep and unvarying affection that it was not dependent upon the intenser joys of physical love. Even before her marriage they must have suspected that Virginia would not be physically responsive, but probably they hoped that Leonard, whose passionate nature was never in doubt, would be able to effect a change.' Virginia's sister Vanessa at first could not understand it. In a letter to her husband, Clive Bell, she writes: 'Apparently she gets no pleasure at all from the act, which is curious. They were very anxious to know when I first had an orgasm. I couldn't remember.' Vanessa's own marriage was actually non-sexual for most of its duration.

Most of Virginia's biographers and commentators on her life and works have assumed that there must have been something wrong, that possibly an early and traumatic experience – when Virginia was sexually assaulted by her half-brother George Duckworth – might have put her off sex forever. But of course, as an artist Virginia knew, if only intuitively, that lack of response to sexual intercourse would leave her more energy available for her work, which was the most important thing in life to her. Spater and Parsons draw attention to the fact that lack of interest in sex did not bother Virginia at all, and that she was probably more relieved than anything else. But it did not affect the happiness of the marriage. Virginia left a suicide note for Leonard which said: 'I don't think two people could have been happier than we have been.'

Virginia Woolf's great friend Vita Sackville-West also enjoyed a non-sexual but long-lasting marriage with her husband Harold Nicolson. Though both pursued affairs with members of their own sex, they remained devoted to each other and wrote notes to each other almost every day of their lives. There is some evidence to suggest that after the birth of her two sons, when Vita renounced heterosexual intercourse, Harold made a few attempts to approach her sexually once more. But as his primary inclination was homosexual, there was little interest on either side in continuing physical relations. The length and happiness of these two marriages indicates that marital content does not depend on sex, and indeed very probably has little to do with it.

One of the most bizarre marriages ever was that between George Bernard Shaw and Charlotte Payne-Townshend. Shaw considered himself a feminist. He insisted that his and Charlotte's bank accounts were kept separate; he also readily agreed to her celibacy clause in the marriage contract. Their marriage, which took place on 1 June 1898, was long-lasting and happy and both continued to remain separate individuals. Shaw was a lifelong vegetarian and passionate anti-vivisectionist. He was also teetotal, whereas Charlotte enjoyed both alcohol and meat (she owned several fur coats, too).

Shaw's views on sex are interesting. He had a deep-seated revulsion to the act of intercourse, and said: 'Nature in a fit of economy has combined a merely excretory function with a creatively ejaculatory one in the same part.' He was convinced that lust – by which he primarily meant male lust – was the chief obstacle to the emancipation of women. He saw no reason why there should be sex within marriage apart from that needed to continue the human race. His feeling was that the 'gratification of amoristic sentiment' was a purely accidental function of marriage, the main advantage of which was that children could be brought up in a stable environment.

Many creative and original people have embraced celibacy in order to pursue their life's work. The well-known Fabian, Beatrice Webb, renounced sex at the age of 26 so that she could dedicate herself to social investigation. It was her belief that 'free love' would lead to madness.

Another famous celibate woman was Florence Nightingale, who was destined by the circumstances of her birth and her place in society to marry a rich man and live a life of leisure. Though she had many suitors, Florence was convinced that she was meant for higher things than marriage and subsequent idleness. Sure enough, in time she dedicated herself to the advancement of the nursing profession. Like Bernard Shaw, who died at 94, Florence Nightingale lived to be a nonagenarian. One cannot say, of course, that celibacy had anything to do with their longevity, but the two may not be entirely unconnected.

The poet Stevie Smith, who now enjoys a cult following, also made a decision to live celibately, and not to have to look after or be responsible for anybody. She remained all her life in the house where she grew up, in Palmers Green, where she was cared for by her 'lion aunt'. Stevie felt she had to remain single in order to write her poems, and regarded herself as a 'friendship girl'. Her biographer, Kay Dick, said in a newspaper interview: 'Stevie was terrified of sex, you know. She had fumblings with men but emotional things with women.'

Yet another famous celibate was the novelist Tolstoy, who was born in Russia into the aristocratic land-owning class, but who later renounced all his estates to become a vegetarian celibate.

Currently, the president of the British Astronomical Society, Heather Couper, shares a home with Nigel Henbest, a fellow astronomer and book collaborator, as she has done since university days. But the relationship, which is permanent, has always been platonic. Heather Couper said: 'We are one another's best friends but sleep in separate rooms . . . I don't want children and never have. I love the stars and the night sky.'

The traveller and writer Jan Morris, who was James Morris until her sex-change operation in the early 'seventies, is also an advocate of celibacy. In her autobiography *Conundrum*, in which she describes how she gradually decided to live as a woman after having been born a normal male, she talks about her unusual marriage. She says:

It was a marriage that had no right to work, yet it worked like a dream, a living testimony, one might say, to the power of mind over matter – or of love in its purest sense over everything else . . . We produced five children, three boys, two girls, but by the nature of things sex was subsidiary in our marriage . . . For months at a time I would wander off across the world and sometimes Elizabeth would travel in a different way, into preoccupations that were all her own . . . The longer we sustained this passionate amity, the less readily I accepted the assurances of marriage guidance counsellors and agony columnists that satisfactory sexual relations were essential to a happy marriage. We could scarcely call our sexual relationship a satisfactory one, since I would have been perfectly happy without any sexual relationship at all, yet our lives were full of compensations. Our intimacy was erotic in a different kind, in a sense of arcane and ecstatic understanding that sometimes a thrust of affection came not as it does in romance, like a lullaby or spring scent, but like a blow between the eyes, a shock to the system . . .

But man and wife, only just . . . The connotation of love with physical sex seems to be a vulgar simplicism, while the overlapping of the two words I consider one of the weakest points of the English language, bred I suppose out of ancient bowdlerisms but now obscene in its own right . . . for fifteen years our marriage looked from the outside not merely successful but perfectly orthodox and when I told the first of my friends the ghastly truth about myself, they often thought I was joking.

Jan Morris put her own lack of interest in sex down to the fact that though outwardly a man, she had felt from her earliest years that she was female, and so the male sexual organs were repulsive to her. Now, many years after the sex change, she looks forward to a time when the messy mechanics of procreation can be overcome, and a cleaner, neater method devised. She hopes that one day the 'clumsy indulgences of coitus will have lost their purpose'. Sex, she declared in an article in the American magazine *Vanity Fair*, is only a device . . . a kindly confidence trick perpetrated by nature for purely functional ends.'

Even in the world of rock music, in which wild sex is often considered normal behaviour, there are devotees of celibacy. One rock star who has come out in favour of celibacy is Steven Morrissey of The Smiths. According to an interview in the *Mail on Sunday*, Morrissey is 'an ascetic who does not smoke, drink, take drugs or eat meat. He lives a life of reclusive celibacy in a neat little house in Manchester.' Morrissey has issued pleas to his vast audience of young people to abstain from all kinds of sexual relations.

He believes that most pop idols sing about life as it is not – while his group's rather mournful songs describe life as it is. His group is successful, he believes, because it is realistic.

Another singing star who has come out in favour of celibacy is the perennial favourite Cliff Richard. Now in his mid-forties and never married, he has said: 'I don't particularly have any great sexual urges or needs, you know. We are all human, but I don't feel I have to spend my life with someone special for sexual favours. But that's my good fortune, isn't it, really? I think sex is important. But it's not a force that's going to destroy me in any way. I have it totally under control.'

Cliff, like many celibate people, has become a vegetarian and eats only one meal a day. He believes it is his ascetic, avowedly Christian lifestyle that has enabled him to remain at the top for almost three decades, while others who were stars in the 'fifties have long since burned themselves out.

Born in India, Cliff Richard has sold more than £100 million worth of records. He recalls: 'I came to the conclusion I wasn't the marrying type. People don't always understand that if you don't have a marriage partner or a girlfriend/boyfriend relationship life does not necessarily come to a dead end.

'I'm getting rebellious about people who say: "Oh it will be so nice when you settle down." I say: "But I am settled." I'm quite happy the way I am. Life is right for me. I have people who love me and people whom I love and that's all that matters. I feel fulfilled.'

The evangelist Billy Graham is convinced that Cliff Richard has no sex life at all, and said so last time he was in Britain on a crusade, in 1984.

Kenneth Williams, the comedian, has always lived alone, and claims he has never been in love. In an interview to mark the publication of his autobiography *Just Williams,* he was quoted as saying: 'I've never felt a desire for anybody. When people come to see me with their problems I think it so weird that they should get worked up about anyone else. Human affection is so ephemeral.'

Williams said he has no sex life at all, and instead puts all his energies into friendships. 'I lead an impeccable life and I am an artist,' he declared. 'I can imagine it without actually doing any of it.'

We know about the views of the people quoted above either because they are in the public eye or they have written about their sexual inclinations. But one suspects that celibacy is actually not confined to a tiny minority of famous, talented or artistic people. It seems that it is far less odd and unusual a condition than we have been led to believe, and also that those following such a life do not have any impression that they are missing anything. On the contrary, they feel that they have gained, and they are free to cultivate and enjoy friendships that leave them still independent and self-sufficient when they so wish. Humans grow by being alone at times, and celibacy offers the opportunity for a genuinely private life.

All those who have freely chosen celibacy mention only the benefits. In our day, though not perhaps in past ages, it has become the harder path to follow.

The majority of us living in the twentieth century have come to feel, with Samuel Johnson, that though marriage may have many pains, celibacy has no pleasures.

Perhaps it is now time to rethink this idea.

Reading list

INTRODUCTION
The Book Book, Anthony Blond (Jonathan Cape, 1985).

CHAPTER 1
History of Western Philosophy, Bertrand Russell (George Allen and Unwin, 1961).
The Hite Report, Shere Hite (Dell, 1976).
Human Sexual Response, William H. Masters and Virginia E. Johnson (Little, Brown, 1966).
Sexual Behaviour in the Human Male, A.C. Kinsey, W.B. Pomeroy and C.E. Martin (Philadelphia, Saunders, 1948).
Sexual Behaviour in the Human Female, A.C. Kinsey, W.B. Pomeroy and C.E. Martin (Philadelphia, Saunders, 1953).
Daily Express, survey, 'Love and the Single Girl' (April 1986).
The Limits of Sex, Celia Haddon (Corgi, 1982).
The New Celibacy: Taking a Vacation from Sex, Gabrielle Brown (McGraw Hill, 1980).
Motivation and Personality, Abraham Maslow (Harper and Row, 1970).
Sex and the Over-forties, Robert Chartham (New English Library, 1971).
The Whole Mind Book, Denise Winn (Fontana, 1980).
Sexual Energy and Yoga, Elizabeth Haich (ASI Publishers, 1975).
Humour Therapy, Branko Bokun (Vita Books, 1986).
Joy of Sex, Dr Alex Comfort (Quartet Books, 1974).
More Joy of Sex, Dr Alex Comfort (Quartet Books, 1977).
Sex and Marriage in England Today, Geoffrey Gorer (Nelson, 1971).

CHAPTER 2
The Republic of Plato, translated by Francis Cornford (Oxford, 1948).

The Guardian, 'Virgo or Virago: St Thecla' by Karen Armstrong (27 January 1984).
Who Walk Alone: A Consideration of the Single Life, Margaret Evening (Hodder and Stoughton, 1974).
Sex in History, Reay Tannahill (Abacus, 1981).

CHAPTER 3

New England Journal of Medicine, 'An Epidemiological Study of Bacteriuria and Blood Pressure among Nuns and Working Women' by Calvin M. Kunin and Regina C. McCormack (21 March 1968).
Collected Works, Vol. 1, Gandhi (Ahmedabad, 1975).
Married Love, Marie Stopes (Putnam, 1918).
Complete Book of Love and Sex, Drs Philip Cauthery and Andrew and Penny Stanway (Century, 1984).
General Practitioner, 'Coital Problems' by Dr David Delvin (1 February 1986).
The Bitter Pill, Dr Ellen Grant (Elm Tree Books, 1986).
Sex and Destiny, Germaine Greer (Secker and Warburg, 1984).
The Vasectomy Book, Marc Goldstein and Michael Fielberg (J.P. Tarcher, 1982).
Understanding Cystitis, Angela Kilmartin (Arrow, 1985).
The G-Spot and Other Recent Discoveries about Human Sexuality, Alice Kahn Ladas, Beverly Whipple, John D. Perry (Corgi, 1983).
The Zinc Solution, Dr Derek Bryce-Smith and Liz Hodgkinson (Arrow, 1986).
London Journal, 1762–3, James Boswell (The Reprint Society, 1952).
AIDS: The Deadly Epidemic, Graham Hancock and Enver Carim (Gollancz, 1986).
AIDS Concerns You, Dr Jonathan Weber/Annabel Ferriman (Pagoda Books, 1986).
AIDS Questions and Answers, Dr V.G. Daniels (Cambridge Medical Books, 1986).

CHAPTER 4

The Listener, 'In Defence of Virgins' by Elaine Morgan (21 July 1977).
Mail on Sunday, article by Germaine Greer (20 January 1985).

Let's Talk about Love (video produced by Responsible Society, 1985).

True Romances, survey (1986).

Love's Mysteries: The Secrets of Sexual Attraction, Glenn Wilson and David Nias (Fontana, 1976).

Pride and Prejudice, Jane Austen (Signet Classics, 1962).

The Incorporated Wife: Oxford Wives and Cambridge Wives, edited by Hilary Callan and Shirley Ardener (Croom Helm, 1984).

Sex and You, Dr Alexander Gunn (Macdonald, 1986).

First Love, First Sex, Kaye Wellings (Thorsons, 1986).

Talking Sex, Dr Miriam Stoppard (Gollancz, 1982).

Look Now magazine, survey on stress (April 1986).

BMA News Review, interview with Gordon Gillick (February 1983).

Sex for Beginners, Dr Eric Trimmer (BMA Family Doctor Publications).

CHAPTER 5

Right-wing Women, Andrea Dworkin (Women's Press, 1983).

Our Blood, Andrea Dworkin (Women's Press, 1982).

Woman's Own, interview with Germaine Greer and Susie Orbach (November 1985).

Sunday Mirror, 'The Great Sex *versus* Cuddles Debate', edited by Joyce Hopkirk (17 November 1985).

Tall Tales, Jerry Hall (Hamish Hamilton, 1986).

The Assault on Truth: Freud's Suppression of the Seduction Theory, Dr Geoffrey Masson (Faber and Faber, 1985).

The Guardian, interview with Dr Geoffrey Masson by Chris Reed (20 February 1985).

Sex and Love, edited by Sue Cartledge and Joanna Ryan (Women's Press, 1982).

What Do Women Want?, Luise Eichenbaum and Susie Orbach (Fontana, 1983).

Over 21 magazine, correspondence column (June 1985).

The Celibate Woman Journal, edited by Martha Allen (Ross Place, Washington, DC).

The Guardian, article on celibacy by Diana Eden (October 1984).

For Yourself: the Fulfilment of Female Sexuality, L.G. Barbach (Signet, 1975).

On Your Own, Jean Shapiro (Pandora Press, 1985).
Pure Lust, Mary Daly (Women's Press, 1984).
Beyond God the Father, Mary Daly (Women's Press, 1986).
Ask Any Woman: a London Enquiry into Rape and Sexual Assault, Ruth E. Hall (Falling Wall Press, 1985).
The Rapist Who Pays the Rent, Ruth Hall, Selma James and Judith Kertesz (Falling Wall Press, 1984).

CHAPTER 6

What Every Woman Should Know about Men, Dr Joyce Brothers (Granada, 1986).
What Makes a Man G.I.B. (Good in Bed), Wendy Leigh (Muller, 1980).
New Internationalist Magazine, article on contraception (August 1985).
Sunday People, 'How to Banish Those Bedroom Blues' by Barbara Jeffrey (17 November 1985).
The Thorn Birds, Colleen McCullough (Macdonald, 1978).
Literary Review, 'The Art of Blockbusters' by Paul Taylor (April 1986).
The Storyteller, Harold Robbins (New English Library, 1986).
Lady Chatterley's Lover, D.H. Lawrence (Penguin, 1961).
Thy Brother's Wife, Gay Talese (Pan 1981).
Holy Virility, Emmanuel Reynaud (Pluto Press, 1981).
Child Sexual Abuse within the Family (CIBA Foundation, 1984).
The Guardian, article on male sexuality by Jonathan Rutherford (27 March 1986).
She magazine, interview with Jenny James (August 1985).
Male Sexuality: the Atlantis Position, Jenny James (Caliban Books, 1985).
You magazine (supplement to *Mail on Sunday*), article by Anthony Burgess (February 1986).
Prick Up Your Ears: a Biography of Joe Orton, John Lahr (Penguin, 1980).
The Sunday Times, 'Every Pin-up Tells a Story' by Helen Mason (January 1986).
The Guardian, 'Sex and the Single Priest' by David Berry (November 1985).

CHAPTER 7

Dr Ruth's Game of Good Sex, Dr Ruth Westheimer (video, Virgin Games).

How to Make Love to the Same Person for the Rest of Your Life (and still love it), Dagmar O'Connor (Columbus, 1986).

The Complete Book of Sexual Fulfilment, Drs Philip Cauthery and Andrew Stanway with Faye Cooper (Century, 1985).

CHAPTER 8

Fear of Flying, How to Save Your Own Life, Parachutes and Kisses, Erica Jong (Secker and Warburg, 1977, 1981, 1984).

'Dear Ann', Ann Landers' column (quoted in *Daily Express*, January 1984).

The Guardian, interview with Dr David Smail (1984).

Vogue Health and Beauty Supplement, 1984, 'Sex and Love: the Crisis of Expectation' by Dr Garth Wood.

Sex in Human Loving, Dr Eric Berne (Penguin, 1970).

An ABZ of Love, Inge and Stan Hegeler (New English Library, 1969).

CHAPTER 9

Augustus John, Michael Holroyd (Penguin, 1976).

Tender Is the Night, F. Scott Fitzgerald (Penguin, 1985).

Celibate Woman Journal, 'Celibacy and the Process of Self-Empowerment' by Dana Densmore (19 February 1983).

Clinging to the Wreckage, John Mortimer (Penguin, 1984).

To the Devil – a Daughter, Dennis Wheatley (Hutchinson, 1962).

Nothing But . . . Christine Keeler, Christine Keeler with Sandy Fawkes (New English Library, 1983).

CHAPTER 10

The New Vegetarian, Michael Cox and Desda Crockett (Thorsons, 1985).

Why You Don't Need Meat, Peter Cox (Thorsons, 1986).

Crime, Diet and Delinquency, Dr Alexander Schauss (Parker House, 1981).

Aphrodisiacs: the Science and the Myth, Peter V. Taberner (Croom Helm, 1985).

The Book of Yoga, Lucy Lidell (Ebury Press, 1983).

Bhagavad Gita, Yogi Ramcharaka (The Yogi Publication Society, Chicago, 1935).

CHAPTER 11

Voltaire in Love, Nancy Mitford (Hamish Hamilton, 1984).

The Heart and the Mind: Voltaire and Rousseau, Guy Endore (W.H. Allen, 1962).

A Marriage of True Minds: Leonard and Virginia Woolf, George Spater and Ian Parsons (Jonathan Cape/Hogarth Press, 1977).

Mrs Woolf, 1912–1941, Quentin Bell (Hogarth Press, 1972).

Vita, Victoria Glendinning (Weidenfeld and Nicolson, 1983).

Vanessa Bell, Frances Spalding (Weidenfeld and Nicolson, 1983).

Ivy and Stevie, Kay Dick (Alison and Busby, 1983).

How Can We Know?, A.N. Wilson (Hamish Hamilton, 1986).

Mail on Sunday, interview with Steven Morrissey by Sarah Gibbings (1986).

Daily Express, interview with Cliff Richard by David Wigg (31 March 1986).

Daily Express, interview with Dr Billy Graham by David Wigg (21 July 1984).

Just Williams, Kenneth Williams (Dent, 1985).

Mail on Sunday, interview with Kenneth Williams by Jane Kelly (15 September 1985).

Index